IF SELECTED

by Alex Russon

ISBN No: 1-904726-90-9

Published by Verité CM Limited for Alex Russon

Cover design, typesetting and production management by
Verité CM Ltd, Worthing, West Sussex UK +44 (0) 1903 241975
Cover llustration by Richard Grundy and Karl Jennings
Printed in England

CONTENTS

ACKNOWLEDGEMENTS

If you'll pardon the indulgence, I'd like to thank a few people for their support in the production of this book...

Richard Grundy, for designing the cover... Jon Clements for setting up the website... Lee Baker for proof reading... Jan Coleman for allowing me to interview her... Rob Hill for his editing prowess... Kate for her proof reading and her editing prowess... and of course the players of St Thomas without whom this book couldn't have been written. C'mon St T's!

The book has a website which may give you a giggle or provide some useful links regarding issues brought up in the book. Hae a wee gander at www.ifselected.co.uk

All proceeds from this book will go to Saltmine Trust and The Hothouse project in Aldridge, Walsall. For more information see the page at the back of the book.

Aldridge St Thomas FC 2006 – 2007

Goalie – Rob Wood Early forties, loves his football, reckons he's a good outfield player but we know different. Doesn't take goal kicks because of a gammy leg. His son Tom runs the line for us.

Right Back – Andy Carter Late teens, accomplished player and serious about his football. You wouldn't want him for a wife, he'd nag you to death, a right grump on the pitch. Gives it everything. Another defender who thinks he's wasted at the back, we all do mate.

Right Back – Tony Walker Goalie's worst nightmare, attempts to display his ball skills in own six yard box while rest of team implores him to "get rid of it". Much loved but injuries catching up with him. Speedy Gonzalez he ain't.

Left Back – Daz Smail Sturdy defender who lets you know you've been in a tackle. The last 50/50 I went into with him in training will be just that, the last. Late twenties I'd guess, quiet off the pitch but plenty to say on it.

Defence – Joe Lister Stalwart of the side and captain. Rarely beaten by a dribbler, takes them out while they're thinking about it. Cavorts forward rather too often for his fellow defenders liking, has been known to go AWOL from his defensive duties but he's captain so what he says goes.

Central Defence – Chris Preece Tall, wins everything in the air and seldom loses on the floor. Mr Reliable of the team, never known to have had a bad game. Sullies the good name of St Thomas by wearing gloves on the pitch.

Central Defence – Clem Triathlete, he's fresher in the last minute than I am in the first. Competent with his right foot, thoroughly incompetent with his left. A great motivator, talks all the way through the game.

Central Defence – Me Natural ball player he is not, appears frightened when it's anywhere near him. Agricultural in his approach, and pedestrian. Not a match winner.

Midfield – Steve Busby Another stalwart, the sitting midfielder spraying the ball hither and thither. Strikes it beautifully except when in front of goal when he slices it like a lemon.

Midfield – Chris Rogers Every team needs one. Fiery is the polite word. Shirker he ain't. Skilful, wholehearted player who takes defeat pretty badly. Better get used to it at St Thomas.

Midfield – Rich Taylor Gives Ian Pearsall a run for best dressed player. Tricky midfielder who scores the odd goal. In and out of the side due to his pastoral duties.

Midfield – John Piggot Performance as he's called (by himself). Similar engine to Clem, same attitude as Chris, if he had the same goal output as Lampard we'd be in business. Has a remedy for any injury but hasn't cured my receding hairline yet.

Midfield – Tom Hathaway Young skilful player, great character. Obtains an obscure injury once a month, ricked neck, swollen eye, never a football injury. Enthusiastic as any in the squad.

Midfield – Nick Jones Another stalwart dedicated to the team for years. Packs a wallop, ball control buys him time and makes up for a somewhat sluggish turn of pace. Silent assassin.

Midfield – Ian Pearsall Clean striker of the ball, has played at a better standard. Refs know how to spell his surname, they scribble it on a weekly basis. Would make a big difference to our side if he could show an aversion to yellow and red cards.

Striker – Matt Brady If games were won on physique we'd be in Europe. Strong forward, holds the ball up for others to play off him. Another who takes defeat personally, he's had good practice.

Striker – Mark Hadden Bucketfuls of goals, he loves every one of them. A pre-season purchase from Grenfell for half a lager and a bag of scratchings. Riles defenders, they rile him, the way it should be.

Striker – Matt Challoner Stan Bowles of St Thomas, crafty imp of a player, scurries around defenders with a polite smile after he's megged them. Bit of a muso, yet to discover Dylan, I'll address this.

Utility – Darren Roberts Right sided player, normally defence. See Tony Walker for description of playing style, has more hair than Tony, but don't we all.

Utility – Vince Letford Loyal clubman of several years standing, rarely able to reproduce his form in training on a matchday, a blessing, believe me. Serving a club enforced six month suspension for wearing a woolly hat and gloves for an entire league match.

Up and coming – Tom Wood After a couple of seasons running the line, Tom will now be old enough to play for St T's. We therefore have a job opportunity, applications are invited for a linesman to flag the opposition offside every time they cross the halfway line.

CHAPTER ONE

"… come on over, the future's here…"

It was big news. Alex Russon, footballing legend in his own lunchtime, was jumping ship to city rivals St Thomas. After five years lumbering around as St Mary's informidable and somewhat hapless centre back, I was defecting. I wasn't the first high profile footballer to cross the city. Mo Johnston played for Celtic before signing for Rangers, attracting a £1.2m fee in 1989. Sol Campbell turned out for Spurs and Arsenal while commanding £20m worth of transfer fees during his career. And now, like them, here I was, joining the elite of city rival turncoats. And the price on my head? £5 administration fee payable to the West Midlands Christian Football League, by myself.

It had been a wrench to leave St Mary's, such a friendly, close knit club and one of the most popular amongst the twenty that existed in the West Midlands Christian Football Leage (WMCFL). It also had one of the largest squads and after four years being guaranteed a place in the starting line up, mostly because no-one else wanted to play centre back, my position was under threat. While I could point to the experience and guile a 37 year old like myself offered the team, the manager quite righty contrasted this with the speed, agility and hunger a selection of 21 year old alternatives now presented. Overnight, the chances of a regular place on the teamsheet began to look shaky for me, the forthcoming football season now stretched out uninvitingly, my involvement every week no longer assured. I'd instead be facing a weekly shiver fest on the sidelines, hoping for a ten minute run-out as substitute if someone fell injured during the match, or worse, the manager might take pity on me ten minutes from time with the game won and throw me on as sub knowing I couldn't do any terminal damage. My pride couldn't take this and I began to think about finding another club.

St Thomas was the obvious option. A recent house move had positioned my wife and I a five minute walk from St Thomas church. We'd been attending for a few weeks now and the manager of the church's football team, Rob Hill, had let me know there was always a place for me if I wanted it. Not because he'd heard of my silky ball skills and weekly man of the match performances (I couldn't boast either), but because his squad rarely numbered more than eleven and he was desperate for more players. "We're not very good and we're in the bottom division," Rob informed me. "We can't win a game of football to save our lives." With such a glowing invitation how could I refuse? I had two major regrets in life and wasn't intent on making it a hat-trick. First, I never saw The Smiths play live and second, I didn't learn an instrument at school. Enough ex-footballers had told me not to retire too early so at the age of 37, despite my receding temples giving me the dilemma of a modest comb-over or whether to get the clippers out for a number one all over, I still felt there was more football in me. The clincher was when I learned that I didn't have to train on a Wednesday evening to earn selection.

The signing ceremony for my high profile move was something of a shambles. Granted, it was a bit much to expect a trestle table in the centre circle pre-kick off, me sat behind it beaming for the cameras, pen poised, while the manager grinned from ear to ear as he stood over my shoulder. It was perhaps too much to ask for us to shake hands before the local media with a St Thomas shirt or scarf held aloft. But I certainly didn't expect the indignity that unravelled itself, giving me a full on beamer as red as the shirts of St Mary's FC... ..

The three churches in the parish of Aldridge, two being St Mary's and St Thomas, had joined forces to organise an event at the local golf club where the Manchester United chaplain, John Boyers, was to provide an insight into his role at the club after we'd scoffed our three courses. Tickets sold out quickly, we hoped for tittle tattle about the club's star players, and many of those attending were from the church's football teams, managers Rob Hill and John Jackaman (Jack) doing an excellent job of rallying their respective troops. I attended with a friend of mine, Force.

Force and I turned up on a cold November evening along with 75 or so others. We took our seats and devoured dinner before listening to an interesting talk by the chaplain. I suppose rather predictably, since he was a man of the cloth, there were no juicy stories about Rooney or Keane to get our teeth into but some interesting comment on the lesser lights. He'd been at the club for many years and noticed a marked difference in the attitude of Scandanavian players like Ronnie Johnson and Ole Gunnar Solskiaer. They were open, friendly and approachable whereas British players appeared guarded and defensive. He'd built good relationships with Christian players such as Tim Howard and Gabriele Heinze but you got the feeling he hadn't built many bridges with non-Christian players, though we were reminded that the Manchester United organisation is not solely about players but also the 500 other members of staff that John as chaplain could come into contact with. He felt he did most of his work with them rather than the players. He ended by reminding everyone in the room that football and the variety of emotions that it disturbed within us, played a large part in millions of people's lives but it needed to be kept in its place. The telling decisions in life weren't about offsides, team selection or which of Rooney's goals were the best of the season. Addressing our thoughts on faith, in particular Jesus Christ, was the stuff of genuine importance and we were left to muse on that as he stepped down from the stage.

After a brief chat with Force I made my way to the bar for a drink. Propping it up and in conversation were Rob Hill and the St Thomas' vicar Richard Taylor, also the church team's midfield dynamo. I ordered my drink and joined in the conversation – yes it had been a good talk, yes the food had been good and no I couldn't stand Man United. Rob agreed with me that the re-run of Man United's finest hour, beating Bayern in the '99 Champions League Final, had been somewhat nauseating and to take our minds off the subject, he reached for his inside jacket pocket and with a flourish, produced a registration form from the WMCFL.

"I brought this along in case you wanted to sign Alex. We're playing the league leaders on Saturday and I've only got nine, we need to make up the numbers," Rob said.

As invitations go this wasn't the most gracious and I could see Richard spluttering over his drink as he smirked in anticipation of my response. I'd have preferred something along the lines of, "Would you do me the honour of signing for St Thomas, we need a player of your calibre to turn our season around," but nevertheless I grabbed the pen from Rob and asked him to turn around so I could lean on his back to sign the form. At that very moment, with Rob's hands on his knees and me tickling his back as I scrawled my signature onto the form, who sidled up to the bar about three feet to my right but Jack, St Mary's manager. I could have died.

Jack began to speak with Tony Walker as they waited their turn to order drinks, both staring at me. They were side on but I felt their gaze, like a laser beaming heat into the heart of me. I hadn't said a word to Jack since pre-season training in the summer and it was now November. We hadn't fallen out, not by any means, but I'd removed myself from training and any involvement with the St. Mary's team months ago. My wife Kate was due to have our first child in the September and I'd thought it an opportune time to step away from football and the indignity of being dropped from St Mary's first team, as a result Jack and I hadn't crossed paths in ages. During that time I'd been talking with Rob about the move to St Thomas but unless Jack had heard this through the grapevine, the first he knew of my impending transfer was right here, right now, as my new manager-to-be was bent double before me as I signed his registration form. I'm not normally short of words but in this instance I was pretty lost.

"Alright Jack?" I offered meekly

"Yes mate, you?"

"Just answering your prayers and joining the opposition" I smiled weakly, deciding self deprecation was the only way out. "No more horror shows at the back for St Mary's, you might stand a chance of getting the odd clean sheet now."

Jack appeared a little bemused but at the same time seemed to sense the awkwardness I was feeling and offered a kind smile.

"I just want a regular game," I went on. "You've got such a difficult job choosing a team out of 20 or so players and at my age I just want to play. Every game could be my last, soon Rob will be hoping that it is!" I chortled, looking for someone around to join in to ease my pain. They didn't. After a period of uneasy silence, Jack stepped forward to bail me out.

"Well the very best of luck Alex, I hope it works out for you," he said. He couldn't have sounded more gracious and privately I wondered if this situation suited him down to the ground, he wouldn't have to give it the old hand on the shoulder routine, muttering, "I'm gonna have to drop you old son."

We chatted for a couple of minutes after Rob straightened up to pocket the signed registration form. I suppose in a perfect world I'd have been happier hearing my old manager plead for me to stay in front of my new manager, to big-up my reputation and convince him what a steal he'd got. Maybe a fist fight in the car park over my signature was too much to ask or a bidding war for my services escalating into the thousands of pounds, but Jack's lack of effort in putting up a fight to retain me was somewhat troubling. In fact the smile on his face as he vigorously shook Rob's hand seemed to unease my new manager who looked nervously across at me as if to say, 'What the hell have I done'. A couple of my new team-mates, including the vicar, looked on with some amusement, they'd clearly taken great delight in the awkwardness of the last couple of minutes. I'm sure when great players are introduced to the dressing rooms of new clubs they aren't greeted in such a manner. I made my excuses, grabbed Force, and left.

The WMCFL was set up in 1979. It has two divisions of ten and it's continued aim is to witness for Jesus Christ in the arena of local football. All clubs are allied to a church, some closely, some loosely, but it's a Christian league through and through. To give you an idea, St Thomas boasts two regular church goers and St Mary's about the same, and that's pretty typical of most teams in the league. The Christians playing in the league see the opportunity to witness their faith to those who either don't have one or find theirs dormant, but this testimony isn't always the greatest. Take me for instance, I've had a collection of yellow cards and some of my tackles are so late they're still to arrive.

Football in the WMCFL is just like any football in any league, feisty, competitive and wholehearted. The only obvious difference being the straight red card awarded to any player who swears. Of the twenty teams, around sixteen are stalwarts with four others coming and going, normally because they're struggling to rustle up eleven players on a Saturday. The basic requisite to league membership, other than church affiliation, is that your club must boast changing facilities at the home ground, though some of the changing rooms might in other circles be regarded as pigeon lofts. We have to take it in turn to get changed because there isn't enough room for us all at once, you bend over to pick your boots off the floor and your backside knocks the next man over. Standards have improved in recent seasons and the graffiti ridden, vandalised portakabins seem to be a thing of the past, though ice cold showers and ill lit, draughty dressing rooms do not. All of the standard cliches can be found on a matchday in the WMCFL, just as in every league, "…Come on boys, do we want this …it's still nil – nil (when your team goes one up) …we're too deep boys, TOO DEEEEP!" They're all there.

The league website declares each result by tea-time. My one remaining ambition is to be shown as a goalscorer without OG next to my name, perhaps then I can equal my tally of own goals (five) and look back at a football career that doesn't end in inglorious deficit. It's only when confessing this that it dawns on me why Jack was stifling a smile when he learned I was leaving St Mary's. There is promotion and relegation between the two divisions, three up, three down, which may seem punitive for those being demoted from such a small division but it keeps the season alive right to the end. There are two cup competitions and we even have proper referees, so they tell us, though linesmen are selected by each team from their bench of subs and this gives rise to some remarkable offside decisions. Matches are played on Saturday mornings at 10.30am providing ample time for participants to reach their favoured Midlands ground later in the day to see how the game is meant to be played (if it's Villa Park they choose). It's a well organised league sitting quietly under the radar of the local amateur football scene and happy to do so.

And so it came to pass on a foggy, crisp November morn, that Alex Russon pulled on the orange shirt of St Thomas and slogged through the mud in the uncustomary position of left back to assist his new team-mates in their fight to a 2-2 draw, away to division leaders City Athletic. I felt at home immediately, slide tackling in the mud, hollering encouragement to team-mates and getting nutmegged by the opposition. I hadn't played since the end of the previous season six months prior and my hamstrings told me so. Thrown on as substitute after 75 minutes to make my low key debut, (I prayed it'd be low key, as a defender coming on late in the game a high profile performance would normally be for the wrong reasons), I was grateful my appearance was to be so short, I wouldn't have lasted another minute. I'd been telling the manager I could change the game for him, I just didn't tell him which way. Naively, I'd declared myself ready for the rigours of football without having exercised in earnest for three months other than the occasional 50 yard 'beat you to that lampost' race with my ten year old son Harry. When the final whistle blew I was wheezing like an old man but had not disgraced myself, to my mind two firm headers and a successful 50/50 challenge outweighed my fresh air shot in the final minute.

Dragging my forlorn carcass off a sloped, windswept pitch, more mud than grass, white markings barely visible and goal nets being taken down by the home team's subs, I shook hands with as many opposing players as I had the energy to approach. I was loving being part of this scene again. Joe Lister piped up, "Three cheers for City Athletic, hip, hip…" but I could only muster the first cheer. I was knackered. I looked up longingly towards the haven of the changing rooms but they were a good 250 yards away, across two unused pitches, over a road and behind the bowling green. We'd have to wait five minutes for the groundsman to open the entrance. It had been a well mannered game, so the five minute delay outside the dressing rooms as we waited for the groundsman, didn't bring forth any handbags. A couple of players smoked cigarettes, a few others spoke on mobile phones, the rest clattered their boots on the slabs to remove the mud from their studs, or exchanged hard luck stories over the 2-2 draw we'd shared. I stood a few yards away looking on, a smile on my face and a leap in my heart, silently basking in the afterglow of my debut for St Thomas and my re-entry to the WMCFL. It was great to be back.

CHAPTER TWO

"… try to change what I've become…"

It was clear after the way I'd staggered to the dressing rooms following my fifteen minute cameo on Saturday, that I needed to start exercising. If I were to play regularly for this team and avoid being either dropped or carried off on a stretcher with ventilation apparatus attached to me, my fitness needed addressing and sharpish. At fourteen stone, I was overweight. I didn't feel it, but when mounting the scales at the doctor's surgery to be informed by the nurse that I bordered on the clinically obese, the issue began to concentrate my mind.

I'd noticed an extra tyre forming lately, an expansion of girth that had crept up on me in the dark and appeared quite happy to settle in for bed and breakfast. The handlebars that crowned my hips were more noticeable each time I undressed. Pulling my shirts and jumpers on, an extra downward tug was needed to hide my protruding belly, and flopping onto the sofa in the evenings I could feel rolls of flesh fold over before cushioning my rib cage. I had formed tiny breasts which drooped forlornly from my chest and my backside could barely be crammed into my suit trousers anymore. My jowls wobbled quite violently when I climbed the stairs these days, even my fingers felt fatter. The final straw came when a friend I'd not seen for a while stood aghast at the "Amount of timber you've put on son." I'd hoped that no-one had noticed my weight gain, and that untucking my shirt or wearing baggier jumpers had hidden the fact, but the moment it was confirmed by a second party, I felt sufficiently moved to address matters. No more take aways and no more cheesecake, I was going straight into a fitness regime, starting today. Right after I'd finished this Twix.

I picked up the phone to my mate Clem and asked him for some advice on how to plan a fitness regime. Perhaps not the smartest of moves, Clem's a triathlete and when I called to request his support he sounded fresh as a daisy after his 16 mile cycle around Cannock Chase. I reckon he was doing one handed press ups while we spoke. He recommended I ought to begin proceedings with a gentle twenty minute jog at Walsall's Arboretum and I took him up on this advice. It was a fair sized park and a place where I felt confident I'd not be recognised. I'd only been there once before, for a kick about with some mates one summer's day, and I wasn't entirely sure of my bearings inside it's walls, but knew a gentle twenty minute jog lay in there somewhere. I didn't fancy getting lost or facing the ignominy of walking back in the dusky nightfall being mocked by people who'd spotted a jogger who couldn't hack it, so for my first outing I decided to run along the perimeter of the park until my watch read ten minutes. I'd then run back completing a twenty minute run in total. That'd do for starters, a simple session to ease me in.

I drove to the park dressed in the shoddiest of running outfits. Never having been a jogger, I didn't know what the accepted dress code was, so had pulled on a mixture of a football and golfing kit; a collared Pringle t-shirt (Kermit green), a pair of Aberdeen FC football shorts from the eighties era (pillar box red) and a pair of office socks (navy) that I'd worn to work the previous day. My lily white legs made a pitiful sight as they disappeared into six year old trainers dragged from the back of the shoe cupboard (Adidas Samba's with the big toe split on the left foot). Some people had all the gear and looked the part, I could not be accused of this, looking as I did like a cross between Rising Damp's Rigsby and Leroy off Kids From Fame.

Having locked my car, I searched for a pocket to put the keys in, I hadn't one, so resolved to slip them in my socks and hope they didn't wriggle their way down to my feet. My first steps as a proper jogger were approaching, I felt strangely nervous and somewhat conspicuous, as if the eyes of Walsall were upon me, their owners ready to hoot their derision at my comical running style. I hadn't been running since cross-country at school and didn't know what to expect, I could quite easily collapse to the floor after five hundred yards or breeze the full distance barely breaking sweat, anything could happen, though I held a pretty firm view as to which of these eventualities was most likely. My football shorts cut tightly into my flesh and my gut hung over the waistband, I wondered how I could be expected to carry this burly frame around the park. Before I'd even taken a step I was feeling doubtful about staying the course, whether that course be five minutes or twenty. No matter, after a shake-out of my arms and legs (I'd seen them do it on the telly), I began to run. Slowly.

Clem had given me a few tips and one came to mind as I made my way from the car park to the beginning of a long, thin tarmac pathway that stretched what seemed like miles into the distance, before winding its way into the trees.

"Don't go off too quick," he'd said. "You'll be knackered in no time if you go haring off and if you're aiming at twenty minutes, you'll have no chance. You'll be dead in five". I did as he said.

It was almost like learning to walk again, my body not used to the actions it was now being called upon to perform. I felt wooden, my legs creaking where they met the trunk of my body and I found trouble positioning my shoulders in order to pump my arms correctly. Should your shoulders be held firm and high or were you meant to allow them to slump to conserve energy? Two minutes in and I was beginning to pant. The mind willing but the body less so as I plodded along like a fifteen year old Daschund being dragged around the park on a lead. And I'd barely started. Again remembering some Clem advice, I thought about the 80% mental, 20% physical rationale that suggested running is very much an exertion of the mind and that your run can be sustained by thinking positively rather than focusing on the woes of your tired body. In an attempt to address this, I lifted my head and began to gaze at my surroundings rather than the path immediately in front. This was a good move. Autumn had brought out the best in nature with trees boasting golden brown leaves, birds chirping and green grass gleaming in the bright sun. There were very few people around, just the odd dog walker and loved up couple, and I felt I was benefiting from a sensation that I'd not had before, a true appreciation of nature. The colours, the aromas, the beauty, all were striking. I must do this more often I mused before returning my attention to the pathway beneath but in so doing, stepped straight back from paradise to hell and began to feel the pain again. Gone were the soothing sights of nature, back came the heavy footed clumpings of battered trainers on unforgiving tarmac.

I took five minutes to reach the trees by which time the dilemma over how to hold my shoulders had been resolved. Whether I wished to or not, I wasn't able to stand tall and strong, and could only stoop as my legs threatened to buckle beneath me. My mind was leaning towards the first of a string of excuses to stop running, that this had been a good idea but hey, it just wasn't for some people and there'd be no disgrace in parking the idea, when I took sight of a row of benches up ahead. Three young women, possibly mid twenties, sat talking, two of them looking my way. From a distance they looked quite attractive and as I approached, more attractive still. Had these benches been vacant I'd almost certainly have perched myself on one of them, ending my exercise there and then, but with one of them now populated by beautiful young women, my male pride kicked in and there was no way I was going to stop. My body was pleading for me to halt, but vanity urged me to continue, and in as stylish a manner as I could muster. Suddenly my back was straightening, shoulders squaring, pace gathering, and as I reached the bench boasting this gaggle of beauties, I attempted a casual smile. I wanted to come over as an experienced runner, a real man, untroubled by physical exertion, capable of reading as I went if I so chose, but the girls weren't to be fooled. My 'smile' as I approached them looked more like a grimace, face stricken with the contortions of a guy who didn't exercise, trying to exercise, pain written all over it, I looked like a constipated baby trying to curl something unpleasant out of itself. It was the forced smile of of a mother-in-law to be who had just been told by her beloved son that he was about to marry the girlfriend she privately hated.

The seated young women sensed my trauma and began to giggle. I felt a pain of embarrassment equal to the pain of fatigue but soldiered on. Like an injured rabbit that runs whimpering into the bushes, I showed them a clean pair of heels, the chastening experience quickening my pace. If I was running fast as I approached them, I was running even faster now in a bid to flee from shame. Once around the corner and out of sight I slowed down to barely a trot.

I passed other people further along the route and found that regardless of their age, looks or sex, I couldn't afford to let them see me stopping, it would be too humiliating. Unwittingly, these perfect strangers were driving me on as I desperately guarded my honour by running myself into the ground to save face. Whatever my motives, I manfully continued and as I approached an expansive, tree lined lake, with a tidy, well kept path circling the water, I felt a second wind kick in which carried me along. Branches hung low almost brushing my hair with their leaves as I trotted anti-clockwise around the lake, scattering the ducks and pigeons that had wandered into my path. Up ahead were two old ladies, grey haired and dressed for winter despite the glorious weather, shuffling slowly in my direction, a white Cairn Terrier walking excitedly alongside. As they drew closer, the ladies looked up, and I offered them a friendly, "Hello." This was a mistake, my simple gesture of goodwill taken as an invitation for conversation at a time when I never felt less able to hold one.

"Lovely day," chirped one, "Have you far yet to run?"

"Pardon?" I replied, expecting and hoping for nothing more than a simple smile or nod from them.

"You look all in, have you far to run?"

"Not far now," I croaked, the second wind gone already. I trotted backwards so as to face them, not wishing to offend.

"It's a lovely to place to run isn't it?"

I smiled weakly, the same smile I'd addressed the bench of young women with earlier, and turned to satisfy rule number one in the rules of running; be facing in the correct direction. I knew it was rude to turn away from the kind old dears, but I couldn't sustain their chat no matter how brief, and a lesson had been learned early in my jogging career; keep your head down and say nothing, do not interact with passers by. Accommodating chat while trying to run was just too much to ask, I must blank people or grunt a reluctant, "Hello" and push on. I wasn't one of these folk able to think and reply on the hoof at the best of times. At the office I felt very much an outsider when the banter between colleagues struck up, I floundered while those around exhibited their quick wittedness, exchanging sharp one liners. To ask me to suddenly be capable of quick conversation while on the brink of physical breakdown would be requiring rather too much. Approaching exhaustion and panting loud enough to frighten squirels from the trees, my mouth was beginning to fill with spittle. I felt self conscious about spitting, but at the same time it was most unpleasant having this well of fluid in my mouth, and believing I was well away from roving eyes, I let forth a discreet emission intended to reach the flower bed a yard or so to my right. I achieved this but only just, and a trail was left on the path between me and it's resting point. I hadn't reckoned on the young mother walking out of the nearby public lavatories with her son on a toddler's leash. She scowled at me, tugged Junior closer towards her and scurried off in the opposite direction.

Glancing at my watch, I noticed the ten minute mark approach, a joyous moment signalling my turn for home, but it was here that the mental games really began. I was exhausted. I'd run non stop for ten minutes for the first time in several years. My shoulders ached, my lungs felt fit to burst and my legs had turned to jelly. The realisation that ten minutes had elapsed was followed instantly with the realisation that ten minutes were still to go, and further, they were bound to be more testing because I was no longer fresh, far from it, I was knackered. I'd started out with something of a spring in my step, and the novelty of the experience had carried me to here, but now I was tiring quickly. How was I going to complete the run without stopping? I'd tried treading lightly hoping the ground didn't notice I was there but that didn't work. Walking now would be a defeat, I'd have failed the test of one simple jog and didn't want to confess that to Clem or to myself, however my mind was passing me messages suggesting I'd done well to get this far and to halt would be excusable. No-one need know and I could amble back to the car congratulating myself on having at least got this running regime in motion, so to speak. I was just beginning to come round to this train of thought when a bunch of kids, around twelve years of age, started to tease me from their vantage point aboard swings and climbing frames next to the wooded area I'd emerged from.

"Run Forest, Run," they chorused. "Speed up you fat bast***."

Pride kicked in, I wasn't about to give these young urchins the satisfaction of seeing me totter gingerly towards the nearest park bench. Instead, I puffed out my chest, squared my shoulders and ran on with a mental picture of myself gliding forward like a swan on still water, serenely cutting the air in a seamless motion, the very epitomy of athleticism. In truth, I looked like a petite woman carrying heavy shopping across Tesco's car park, though perhaps not as fast.

I pressed on, labouring all the way back to the car park, leaving behind the taunts of youngsters, the protracted conversation of oldies, the disparaging curses of a young mother and the beauty of nature, which today had truly been unveiled to me. Finally I was able to stop as I reached my car, placing both outstretched hands upon it as if I were pushing it up a hill. I panted like a hot dog for a full two minutes, expecting my lungs to reach up through my throat and spill themselves onto the ground. Once satisfied that I wasn't going to vomit or collapse, I let out a couple of deep sighs before returning to full height, my exhaustion soon replaced by mild euphoria as I looked back, with not a little satisfaction, at the course I'd just completed. I'd come, I'd seen, I'd conquered, and smiling smugly, I reached inside my sock for the car keys that would see me home to a hot, refreshing shower and a well deserved night in. It was Arsenal v Spurs on Sky tonight, should be good, a spicy local derby. But rummaging around in my short socks I wasn't able to find the keys…

… instead I was to find them forty five minutes later, lying in a puddle by the lake, having made their way over the top of my short, navy office socks which had been gradually riding down my ankles as I ran. I trudged back, passing the giggling women and the triumphant, mocking urchins. I was walking this time, too exhausted to impress. I'd invest in zip up pocketed shorts for my next run, or longer socks.

CHAPTER THREE

"… we're goin' over the country and into the Highlands to look for a home…"

Christmas was upon us and it was to be the first with our new daughter Emily, now three months old. One day is the same as the next in infant world but not in the world of two new parents, proud as punch of their new addition and eager to experience Christmas for the first time together. It's a time when I normally struggle to be honest, Christmas Day is fine but the down-time surrounding it leaves me climbing the walls, I don't do relaxation. But this year would be different.

The week before Christmas, we travelled to Scotland to visit our family and do the present distribution thing. Kate's family live near Aberdeen, mine are spread between St Andrews on the east coast and Troon on the west, so from our Walsall starting point there were a fair amount of miles to cover over the four days. The first two legs of the journey saw us on the East coast, braving the chill winds off the North Sea and sliding around the dual carriageway as the big freeze began. Fife and the Grampians are beautiful parts of Scotland, largely overlooked by tourists who flock to the west coast, drinking in the beauty of the mountains. The east is certainly a starker terrain and with snow covered mountain tops above rolling hills of frost and bare trees, it appears starker still. It has an attraction of its own, long expanses of hills, fields and farms until a corner is turned and the vast North Sea washes towards the coastline.

In no time though, we found ourselves leaving Aberdeen and on the opposite side of the country looking out at the Isle of Arran from the beaches of Troon. We'd had our couple of days with my mother then Kate's parents, now it was the turn of my father. Within ten minutes of our arrival he'd decided his dog Jake needed a walk and we took the opportunity to stretch our legs too. My father has changed since I was a child, he has become quite an eccentric and now that he's into his sixtieth year I can only see it getting worse. In one respect he remains the same, he's as careful now with money as he ever was. Fastidious is the polite word, or prudent, I'm sure Gordon Brown had my Dad firmly in mind when establishing 'prudence' as his watchword. Dad would go a long way to get a deal, and I suppose the best example of this would be bringing forward his 60th birthday celebrations by two years so he could take advantage of a half price offer for a cruise around Europe. He'd always wanted a fortnight long Mediteranean cruise in summertime to mark his 60th. He ended up with a European cruise for one week in the winter when he was 58, because it was 'on offer'. That's my Dad.

Careful and measured as he is with money, he's completely impulsive when it comes to day to day living, or rather minute to minute living, because everything with my father occurs in a whirlwind. You can get up at eight in the morning when on holiday with him, with your day mapped out before you, yet when you retire to bed that evening it would have taken an entirely different course than the one planned. Spontaneity is an asset in someone, it keeps life interesting, but try telling that to a 10 year old boy expecting a day on the water slides at Aquapark who discovers at the death he's off instead to see an Italian basilica. But as I grow older, where before I found my father frustrating, he's now endearing, though not always...

Kate and I shuffled into Dad's kitchen the morning after our arrival.

"Morning you two, sleep well?" he asked merrily before turning away without waiting for the answer. He rarely acknowledges a response, his mind's moved on.

"Not really Dad. The ceiling caved in and we were robbed in the night. Kate got knifed!" I replied.

"Good, good. Right then, what's it to be? A fry up or sausage sandwiches?"

We tried to request sausage sandwiches but he wasn't taking that for an answer. He'd decided on a fry up and a fry up it was to be. As a teenager I used to boil inside when he'd give me two options only to completely ignore my choice and choose whatever was most convenient for him. These days I just let it blow over me.

"Pour yourselves a cup of tea, there's a bit left in the pot," he insisted, spraying the frying pan with what looked like window cleaner.

"Great idea this, have you seen it? You spray the cooking oil on instead of pouring it, lasts much longer and you don't use too much fat." He loved inventions like these, he was easy to buy for at Christmas.

I poured a cup of tea and was two sips in when Dad piped up, "You'll be Jakey's friend for life if you tip some of that in his bowl when it cools down, he loves tea." I looked blankly at the dog, no-one interferes with my first cuppa of the day, good books or not. Jake licked his lips and whimpered but that wasn't going to sway me.

Dad saw this exchange between man and beast and decided to take matters into his own hands. Lurching forward, he grabbed my cup of tea and in an instant tipped more than half of it into Jake's bowl. Handing it back to me he laughed, "There's more in the pot," before turning to continue with his cooking. Jake began to lap from the bowl but stopped immediately, his tongue scolded by the piping hot tea. He stepped away looking somewhat bewildered while I looked forlornly at my cup which my father was now re-filling with the teapot's stewed remains. The first cup of the day had in a flash become a lukewarm cup of orangey brown liquid that I could stand a teaspoon up in. My father returned to his stove with a whistle and a snatch of, "New York, New York" while Jake and I exchanged bemused looks. This was my Dad, interfering with the best of intentions but leaving a mess behind him while carrying on, oblivious to the commotion.

"Now you know I've got work today Al don't you?" Dad announced.

"Yeah no problem, you've booked a half day, you're going in after lunch, yes?"

"Well not quite, I've to be in for 11 I'm afraid, there's some cheques to sign and I'm the only authorised signatory" he explained earnestly. I was a little disappointed, thinking we'd be able to spend more time together since Kate and I were driving back to Walsall at lunchtime, but didn't mind really, we'd arrived at tea-time the previous evening and managed to spend a few hours in Dad and his wife Kim's company.

"Do you still get the bus in to work?" I asked.

"Yes Al, well normally, but I thought I'd take the train today if you wouldn't mind running me to the station. It leaves at 10 so we'll need to go at 9.40, let's say 9.30 to make sure."

In the end my Dad had us out the door for 9.15 so he could pick up a paper and a sandwich on the way. Thus the proposed morning we were going to share together never materialised. No harm done but again, typical of father's random behaviour.

Before we left the house for the drive to the train station, he decided he must have a photograph of Kate, Emily and me, so went in search of his camera. Ten minutes later he returned and after finally finding one end of it from the other, asked us to huddle together. After a few seconds behind the lens, one eye squinted and his knees bent, he stood back up to his full height having not taken the photograph. We stayed in photographic pose wondering why the delay and waiting for him to crouch back down again, but he didn't.

"I'm not sure this is a good idea Kate, you've just got up and don't look your best do you?" he said. Kate was mortified. Sure enough she was in her dressing gown and had neither washed nor brushed her hair but Dad's concern seemed a little misplaced. I smiled at him thinking it was a joke, Kate smiled nervously wondering if she'd misheard, Dad put his camera down and walked towards the back door to let the dog out. He was serious. Tact in my father's language is a word describing what's happened to a succesfully laid carpet.

"Okay, the dog's out, could you keep an eye on him please Kate, I've gotta get off to work. It's been terrific seeing you, look after that little one for her Grandad won't you?" And with that, the whirlwind left.

We drove home to Walsall in good time and after a couple more days at work, the Christmas holiday began. This year it seemed to go on forever. I finished work officially on December 22nd and planned to return on January 2nd though hadn't taken leave during the interim, there was no point. Working as a salesman for a bank, no-one wanted to see me between Christmas and New Year so I simply tucked myself away at home for the most part, waiting for the phone to ring, which it didn't.

There was though the welcome interruption of a football match. A friendly on December 30th versus St Matthews. We'd been two weeks since our last game and with a busy January programme coming up, Rob reckoned a few cobwebs needed blowing away today, rather than next Saturday after we'd gone 2-0 down. He texted us on the Thursday and announced we'd be playing on astroturf, this presented an instant problem. I had no trainers for astroturf and football boots would be out of the question unless I wanted to skate around like Bambi on ice, turning an ankle or two. So I made for Sports Soccer.

In my opinion, shopping at any time is a neccessary evil, but at Christmas time it becomes worse than evil. The retail park was teeming with kids and fractious parents marching grimly from shop to shop, exchanging Christmas Day's unwanted presents for vouchers, buying bargains, queueing, queueing and queueing. It was packed. I decided a smash and grab raid was in order, no window shopping, no three quotes from three shops, just a bee-line for Sports Soccer, a swift purchase, then home. But first I needed to get my motor parked, this in itself taking thirty minutes as a 'one in one out' system at the car park was administered by a gleeful looking gateman. He couldn't care less about the frustrations of drivers and pedestrians crowding in on him from all angles, he was getting paid for witnessing their exasperation and appeared to be loving it. With a smile and a wave he'd lift the barrier for one car to leave while nonchalantly lifting another with a friendly wink to the incoming driver. He looked warm and comfy inside his hut, tee shirted while those around hunched their shoulders against the cold. He probably had Jonathan Ross serenading him from Radio 2's airwaves and the tall flask sat before him suggested he wasn't going without refreshment. Finally it was my turn to receive his wink and grin, but that was the easy part, I now had to search for that one vacant space in a car park housing a thousand vehicles, I'd have been quicker finding a needle in a haystack.

There's a sensation of enormous smugness as you lock your car up in a packed car park and walk off whistling, while cars circle, their engines coughing back into life once their owners realise you were coming not going when you finish fiddling your car into position. I try not to look at the driver's faces as I walk those first few steps but now and then I will, normally to find a bloke harrumphing to his family, "Bugger ain't goin'" or words to that effect. I skipped to Sports Soccer and within ten minutes found myself skipping back again, a fifteen quid pair of Umbro cheapos tucked under my arm. I hadn't tried them on, I couldn't be bothered and anyway it would be pointless since I have one foot a full size bigger than the other, no footwear ever fits me. The shop had been surprisingly quiet and rather than push my luck by dilly dallying as the shop filled up, I coughed up my money and scarpered. I'd never worn astroturf trainers before and didn't even know how they differed from normal trainers, when I was a kid trainers were trainers but not these days. The shop assistant bundled a pair into my hands saying "These are what you're looking for mate" and I was only too pleased to take his advice. There were nobbly bits on the underside which I assumed gave a player a better grip of the surface but that aside, they didn't look any different. Again as a youngster, I'd have poured over every pair of trainers in the shop, you had to have just the right ones at school or your friends mocked you, but at 37 I couldn't give two hoots.

Saturday came and with it the St. Matthews game. I turned down the offer of a lift to the venue, Willenhall's 'Goals', knowing I'd have to zip away upon the final whistle to collect my children Harry and Hattie from their Tamworth home. The weather was cool but not oppressively so, the grey skies threatening a downpour at any moment. Punctuality I'm a stickler for so I was there in good time and chatted with our keeper Rob who sat waiting in the car park.

"Didn't see you at our Christmas drink the other night," he said.

"Couldn't make it I'm afraid, not my scene these days."

"Weren't anyone else's scene neither," Rob chuckled. "Only three turned up. The rest were recovering from a bender the night before."

I'd received the invite but politely declined on the grounds that a bawdy night out with the lads around Christmas time wasn't the cleverest place for a recovering alcoholic to find himself. It had been almost three years since my last drink but there's never room for complacency and I wasn't prepared to take the risk. "Remember — people and places" Peter my counsellor and friend had told me in the early days and it's advice I dwell on often. "Only 7% of people who quit drinking manage to maintain their sobriety," he'd also told me and I'd rather he hadn't. I was only three months in at the time and to be told 93 out of 100 recovering alcoholics failed made me feel like surrendering there and then.

The stragglers arrived over the next fifteen minutes and to manager Rob's relief it soon became clear that we could field a side of eleven. Mark Hadden had driven over from his shift at Solihull Hospital, Clem had appeared for his St Thomas debut after years with me at St Mary's, Steve Busby and centre back Preece were present despite suggesting they may be otherwise, the nucleus of the side were indeed present except for Nick Jones who was getting to grips with nappy changing for the first time after his wife had given birth recently. Matt Brady was reputed to be at his girlfriend's in Coventry engaging in a similar activity to that which Nick Jones had been engaged in nine months or so prior. The rain started so we dived into the changing rooms.

'Goals' is a footballing complex comprising twenty six-a-side pitches and a couple of eleven-a-sides. The changing rooms are communal so when we entered and saw a team of 40+ year olds clambering into their yellow football kits our hearts leapt, this was going to be a doddle. Perhaps St Matthews had struggled to raise a team and had dragged in fathers and ex-footballers from the congregation. Sadly we were mistaken as the wrinkled gentlemen took to the 6-a-side pitches before the proper St Matthews filed in, looking decidely younger, fitter and sharper. I recognised a number of them and knew I was in for a run around, spotting a couple of familiar strikers changing into the all grey St Matts kit (horrible it is, bit like Newcastle away in the '80's, the Beardsley and Gascoigne era). I often do recognise opposing players, but feel like something of an invisible ever present myself, five years in the league and I doubt a single player from another team would recognise me, but this is actually a blessing in disguise. On the one hand recognition would mean I was a world beating matchwinner who nobody could forget, but on the other, I could be the hapless whipping boy that strikers can't wait to line up against knowing the easy ride they're in for. Believe me, there are players in our league who carry such a burden.

The full sized outdoor pitch was surrounded by a thirty foot high wire netting that at first glance appeared unlikely to be scaled even by the heftiest of hoofs, but the following ninety minutes disproved this theory. The three substitutes would regularly be scurrying after clearances and wild shots, it was just as well there were three spare footballs to allow the game to keep running. Before the game commenced I observed the first of the obvious differences between my new and former teams, the warm up. St Mary's have one, St Thomas don't. Previously I'd be forming a circle with my team-mates as we went through a range of stretches before trotting from touchline to touchline in a vigorous warm up to stave off injury and freshen us up before the kick-off. St Thomas however had a different approach, it involved clouting the practice balls randomly around our half of the pitch with the goalkeeper occasionally having his fingers warmed by a shot. I say occasionally because most of the attempts troubled only the wire netting behind the goal or dog walkers ambling across the adjoining field. Stretches were performed by only John Piggot (Pig), as you'd expect since he's a sports injury consultant, and Clem. The rest of us continued to smash balls around with no obvious target in mind until the referee called the captains together and we were off.

I lined up at left back. I'd told Rob I was a defender and nothing else and he acted accordingly when positioning me. I couldn't score goals, couldn't pass a football much beyond ten yards and hadn't dribbled since a baby. My sole function as a footballer was to stop people enjoying themselves with strong tackles, firm headers and long clearances. I was your no frills type of player if you will, never taking more than one touch at a time. While others delighted in hogging the ball and charging off on mazy runs with the ball at their feet, I was only too happy breaking up attacks from the opposition with a hoof, clatter or barge. I loved it. On astroturf though, slide tackles were out unless I wanted to give my legs carpet burns, so 25% of my game was now rendered redundant and, placed at left back rather than centre back where I'd played for years, it wasn't likely I'd see many headers so that was another 25% gone. This left me with two aspects of my game to focus on, hoofed clearances and playing the opposition on-side. I carried these duties out with aplomb as the game progressed but had the good fortune to find, on both occasions when I messed up, that our manager was marching off to retrieve a ball from over the fence so didn't see my mistakes.

I viewed today's game as one of significance where I was concerned, despite it only being a friendly. Rob didn't know much about me as a footballer, only what I'd told him and I'd predictably bigged myself up over recent months. Now here I was in the flesh having to substantiate my claims of being a rugged defender and I felt that were I to have a good game, it may cement my place in the side and I could expect to be selected on a regular basis, which was the sole reason I'd left St Mary's for St Thomas.

The game began in a swirling wind and I had plenty of time to acclimatise to my new team as the ball spent the first ten minutes up the other end with us on the attack, using the following wind to its best advantage. Then came my first involvement, the type an amateur footballer fears, their keeper delivered a massive clearance towards the halfway line which steepled into the sky before making it's way towards me. Like a cricketer anticipating the flight of ball as he attempted a catch, I tip toed backwards with my neck arched skyward until the ball was upon me, then I attempted a header. I was under it, under it, hold on, it's going over me, noooo... ..it's gone, and the next I knew I was turning around chasing after their right winger as he bore down on goal. He missed the target with his shot but that couldn't disguise my mistake. I hitched up my shorts, looked at the floor as I walked back to my mark and gave myself a talking to. A great start. That needed to be my last blunder or I'd have Rob dredging the congregation for footballers again.

Thankfully it was my final mistake. The ball was kind to me thereafter and spent most of the game on the opposite wing where I couldn't do any damage. On the odd occasion it did fall my way I treated it with the disrespect I felt it deserved and without fuss, clattered it away from danger until the eighty minute mark came and I called over to Rob for him to replace me with our sole substitute, I needed to get off to collect my kids. The game ended with the same scoreline as I had left it, 2-2. The first half was scoreless but after we'd gone ahead a minute into the second half, St Matt's quickly replied with two goals, the first of which was the stuff of farce. They lofted a through ball over our central defence at the very moment that Chris, our central defender, ran off the pitch to get home for a prior engagement. Our other central defender, Joe, had assumed the game had been suspended by the referee while a substitution was made, but was mistaken and a gleeful centre forward ran through to slot the ball into the net. No harm done, it was only a friendly and besides, Mark Hadden notched an equaliser for us late on so it hadn't cost us the game.

I drove to Tamworth happy with my morning's work. It had been my first full game (almost) for my new team and I felt part of it already. The guys in the team were friendly, my mate Clem was in the team too which made me feel at home and I'd given a good enough account of myself to expect selection for the match next week at Chawn Hill. That's until I saw Rob at church the next day and he dropped an unwelcome hint that I may be counting my chickens a little prematurely. As Kate and I left church, he bent down over the pram to speak to our baby Emily.

"Hope you're not keeping your old man up at night young lady," he cooed.

"No danger, sleep through anything me," I quipped.

"Cos I need him awake *just in case* he's picked next Saturday."

I didn't like the just in case element of his sentence and worried about it all week in the lead up to the Chawn Hill fixture. I wanted to play football, not catch cold on the subs bench.

CHAPTER FOUR

"... asked you for nothing, that's what I got..."

I returned to work, after the Christmas break, only having to move ten feet from my pillow to do so. I work from home, our nearest office being 180 miles away in Basingstoke, so my spare room is rigged up, like millions today, with computer, printer, fax and an internet connection. I'm contactable via my work's mobile phone too. There really is no need for a salesman like me to be in an office since I spend most of my time travelling the Midlands, visiting customers and bank branches. It can be lonely but when the cricket's on telly in the Summer, I find working from home has it's benefits.

The first visit of the New Year was to Brierley Hill, a metal fabrication firm that needed to borrow money. The bank couldn't lend this company any more money via the traditional overdraft method (sorry for the bank speak), so I was wheeled in by the bank manager as the best option for Mr Leigh and his business. I 'sell' factoring facilities. I say 'sell' but that's not really my style, I simply present a product before a company and leave them to decide whether it's for them or not. I won't bore you with the intricacies of domestic non-recourse factoring facilities and the benefits thereof, believe me you wouldn't want to know and I can't have readers nodding off as early as chapter 4.

I met Mr Leigh at his home rather than his business premises. Strictly speaking he wasn't back at work until the following Monday but he was happy to welcome me from the comfort of his armchair during his holidays so serious had his business' financial situation become. His was one of these new build houses on a busy street alongside other new build houses that looked exactly the same, except for different coloured front doors and garages. Its' Cotswold style brickwork towered three storeys into the sky, five bedroom gaff minimum was my guess, and the driveway comfortably housed my car next to three others, it looked like the whole family was lying in wait for me. A frail, wispy bearded 60 year old gruffly answered the door, his wrinkled skin suggesting decades of chain smoking. He was dressed casually but smartly, a pristine V necked sweater over a checked collared shirt, both looked fresh out of their Christmas wrapping paper. This was Mr Leigh. Seeing the deep piled cream carpet stretching through the hallway before me, I offered to take my shoes off, but he muttered that there was no need unless I'd walked through a field to get here.

There's a lot to be said for the old adage that 'first impressions count'. I know what atmosphere a meeting will be held in as soon as the greetings and small talk are exchanged, and already I was feeling that my first appointment of the New Year was going to be a cold affair. We sat down in his cream carpeted lounge, dominated by the largest flat screen television I'd ever seen. New build though it was, there was plenty of evidence of old style decor, unsightly squirly patterned wallpaper stretching across the walls, further adorned by poor quality paintings and aged family portraits. The brown sofas had massive arm rests and you sank into the settee like a motor racing driver lowering himself into a car's bucket seat. A foot rest popped up as I disappeared into the back of my chair, I carefully replaced it, a business meeting is not best conducted when the salesman is sat back as if relaxing on Blackpool beach.

We continued to exchange lame pleasantries with the best of intentions but both sensed we were going through the motions and quickly turned to business. In short, Mr Leigh had a £25,000 overdraft which needed increasing and the bank had said no. His best option now was to have an advance against his invoices from me which would provide him with the £50,000 he believed he needed. But first I needed to establish that we could offer our services to his business, certain criteria needed to be met, so my interrogation began.

"Tell me Mr Leigh, how long have you been trading for?"

"Twenty years," he replied abruptly.

"And always in the same trade or has the business changed direction over the years?"

"Been metal bashin' since day one," he mumbled, already appearing to lose interest.

"Do you have many customers?"

"Four." I waited for him to expand but there was nothing more.

This was becoming awkward. In my fifteen years experience in sales I'd learned the best way to conduct a business meeting was to ask simple questions and let the respondent wax lyrical with his answers. Small business owners love talking about their businesses, it's their little baby, and normally a simple question along the lines of, "tell me about your business" proved the catalyst for a proud outpouring of the company's history since birth. This saved me asking several other searching questions because the answers were volunteered without request. But not today.

"Ahem," I coughed nervously. "And how much money is your business owed by your customers as we sit here today would you say?" A satisfactory answer to this question would enable me to dive in and tell him how much our product would suit him.

"Dunno," he replied.

"Just approximately," I said.

"Dunno."

I took a deep breath without making it obvious. Here I was representing the bank in an effort to save this man's business from falling over and he was proving obstinate. I tried a different tack.

"You currently have an overdraft of £25,000 Mr Leigh, how much do you feel you need, to pay off creditors and keep the business running?" I enquired, a little more sternly now.

"Didn't she tell yer, that manager of mine? Bleedin' useless, just don't talk to each other do yer?" was his considered response. I knew what the answer was but needed him to spell it out so I could focus him on the magnitude of his company's situation.

"Well Sir, we can potentially make available 80% of the amount which you're owed at the moment, do you feel this would represent the figure you need?"

"Could do, dunno," was his response, before calling his labrador off my knee and ushering him outside to the kitchen, closing the lounge door behind him. Sat there alone now, I stared through the patio doors out to the bland garden with it's square lawn, empty flower beds and orange coated timber fencing. I took another breath, this one more extravagant since there was no-one there now to take offence. I could have stayed at home today, it was only January 2nd and most folk hadn't returned to work, I'd been unlucky to be called out. I could've been bouncing Emily on my knee, cooing gibberish to her while she beamed back at me, Sky Sports keeping me posted on today's Scottish football action. Instead I was in Brierley Hill, attempting to draw blood out of a stone that had disappeared out to the kitchen with his mutt. He hadn't even offered me a cup of tea.

Ten minutes ticked by during which time I heard happy high pitched conversation through the walls, presumably Mr Leigh had forgotten about me and joined in the conversation with his family in the neighbouring room instead. His belly laugh irked me, he'd barely given me the benefit of a smile and had been completely uncooperative as I took steps to save his ailing business, yet here he was now rattling the timbers with his belly laughs. After another group giggle from the family, his voice grew louder as he left them to return to me.

"I've got to go out, could you come another time?" he announced unabashed, offering this not as a question but as a statement. My expressionless face stared back at him as I digested his announcement, he looked equally blank faced as he waited patiently for an answer.

Your mind races along so many tangents at moments like this, you struggle to find the words that express your emotions while still trying to remain polite. When you work for a high street bank particularly, you're conscious that you're representing a household name, a brand, that everybody knows or has heard of and there's a certain diplomacy expected from its staff. You don't like being rude in any walk of life but when you're working for the bank there is a certain weight of responsibility you feel upon your shoulders. Unless it's just me. I hesitated further before replying but he seemed happy to wait, he wasn't going to bail me out by offering profuse apologies or changing his mind. I wanted to tell Mr Leigh that I had better things to do than drive around the Midlands visiting timewasters who couldn't spare an hour with someone who could potentially save his business from ruin. I wanted to tell him where he could stick his company, his naff wallpaper and his swimming pool sized flat screen TV, but I resisted. I silently bent down to pick up my laptop as I collected my thoughts then stood upright to give him the toned down version of my thoughts. But he beat me to it.

"My cousin's back from Canada for Christmas and we're 'avin a bit of a booze up. I've gotta go I'm afraid."

'Count to ten' my mother used to say. I got to nine but still trembled with rage. My cheekbones were prominent as I grated my teeth hard, if I opened my mouth and spoke there was no telling what I'd say. His business was on the brink of capitulation, I'd travelled across town to his home when I could've been making myself a cup of tea that he hadn't the decency to organise for me, and he was curtailing our joke of a meeting because he had a pint of bitter with his name on it, waiting at the The Navigation.

I resisted the urge to bop his hooter and simply said, "I'll be off then," as I reached down to collect my belongings. I returned to my full height to find him gone, he'd pushed off to freshen up already, leaving me to show myself out. Hmm. The working year had got off to a marvellous start. I let myself out, the gaggle of family members in the front room too beset with uncontrollable giggling to bid me farewell, or even notice I was there. Shutting the front door behind me, the festive wreath wobbling with the force with which I slammed the door, I marched to my motor resisting the temptation to drag my keys down the side of his personalised number plated Merc. Waster. He'd only have himself to blame if his business went pop while he was lording it in the boozer. That's the thing with this job, you get good visits and bad ones, warm people and obstinate ones, those that view their relationship with the bank as vital to the financial success of the business and those who wouldn't piddle on a bank if it were on fire. He clearly had nothing but contempt for us and the feeling was now somewhat mutual.

I had a good job all in all, there weren't many appointments as poor as this, and in a funny sort of way, the variety of people I came across in my working week made life interesting. I'd met bolshy sales focussed mercenaries, warm, gentle husband and wife company owners operating from their cosy cottage, tattooed and bojangled haulage company owners and even an orange faced, hairpiece wearing pornographer bringing in adult films from abroad to sell to sex shops across the country. Mr Leigh wasn't the first awkward customer and neither would he be the last. I hoped he enjoyed his session this afternoon, but when his hangover wore off and he realised his company was dangling by a thread tomorrow morning, he could drive to me the next time. The kettle wouldn't be boiling though.

CHAPTER FIVE

"... you were on the straight and narrow, you were going round the bend..."

January 6th, the day Christmas festivities officially end as people drag down their decorations on twelfth night. Today, it was also to represent the beginning of a new year for St Thomas FC. We wanted promotion and we wanted to win the cup and it started here in a cup match against last season's league champions Chawn Hill (notice I'm saying we already?). It had taken a lot of soul searching to leave St Mary's but now I'd done it I was all out for promotion and cup success with my new team.

The cup competition format had changed a couple of seasons back. Instead of a straight knock-out, it now began as a mini league with the winners of each of the four leagues going into the semi-finals. Our opponents were to be St Mary's (!) who we'd already lost to before I joined, Brierley Hill who we'd beaten, Amblecote and Chawn Hill, both of whom we'd yet to play. More than one defeat would signal a certain exit from the competition and we'd had our one defeat already, so today was a must win. And it was away at the league champions.

The day started for me at 6am when 4 month old Emily announced herself, my hopes that she was hungry and needed feeding by her mother soon dashed when Kate rolled over and confirmed she'd fed her only an hour or so prior. I dragged myself out of bed and carried Emily downstairs to our living room, the normal routine ensuing, her sat in her bouncy chair being cooed over for ten minutes before a settled mood had been established so I could strut into the kitchen and make a cup of tea. Being the father of two children before Emily, I felt a little superior when it came to caring for a baby. I'd learned how to settle her first thing in the morning and once done, I could spend an hour or so surfing on the internet or reading, while Emily occupied herself with her baby gym or, whisper it, the television. What's the old adage when choosing a house? Location, location, location. Well to my mind the watch word when bringing up a baby was routine, routine, routine and this included the first couple of hours of the day. I had it simple really. She was a wonderfully settled baby but had her moments, never though in the first two hours of the day, the time I always spent with her before getting ready for work or beginning the weekend. As soon as she became fractious, normally 8am, it was over to Mummy for breast feeding.

I switched on the computer to visit Simplyswitch.com, I'd heard a few minutes spent on this site would save me money on my utility bills. So many providers, so many products, it was mind boggling. Many of the energy providers I'd never heard of and though they were offering significant savings, I was reluctant to give them my business, you know the sort of thing, don't buy off someone you don't know. I settled on a kind of halfway house, switching to a company that I'd heard of, saving a decent amount of money but having the comfort of knowing who I was dealing with. So I hoped. Truth is they're just a name, I know them no better than I know the Queen's corgis.

A cup of tea washed down my pre-match meal, the remains of last night's chicken jalfrezi from the Indian take-away, then I packed my sports bag. By 'pack', I mean check that my football boots and shinpads are in the bag, they always are because there they've remained since the previous match. I can't imagine Thierry Henry's big match build up involving a curry and the packing of a solitary plastic bottle of Morrison's own label spring water. I pulled on a pair of jeans and the nearest t-shirt and sweater I could find, and was out of the house after my goodbyes to Kate and Emily. The car was littered with splintered poppadum pieces from the night before so I polished them off for good measure. Kate's never seen a poppadum from our Indian take-away, they've always been scoffed by the time I return home.

The meeting point for today's away game in Stourbridge, was to be Anchor Meadow car park. St Thomas used to play at Anchor Meadow's playing fields before moving to The Stick & Wicket this season and this was a welcome switch. It wasn't nicknamed Anchor Muddoh for nothing, you'd find yourself ankle deep in the stuff nine times out of ten, matches becoming a survival of the fittest as we slogged and slipped our way through ninety minutes. Newly formed team, Walsall Olympic, now had the misfortune to claim this place as their home ground, I don't know who cleaned their kit but whoever it was had a job on their hands.

Clem and Chas had arrived before me and the three of us exchanged idle banter before the others drove up, and there were lots of them. Rob Hill for the first time since he set the team up ten years ago, found himself with an embarrassment of riches, seventeen declaring a willingness to play. He only needed fifteen for a sensibly sized squad, and that was probably two too many. Just my luck I thought, I join another club in order to get a regular game because they can barely scramble eleven together on a Saturday morning and here I am on the brink of being sent home before we leave the car park.

"Crikey. There's twelve of you 'ere with five on the way. I feel like Alex Ferguson picking from a squad this big," Rob laughed nervously, knowing he was going to have to disappoint someone. He shifted uncomfortably in his shoes, scratching the back of his head, who was he going to turn away? I looked at him with my best hang dog eyes, trying to appeal to his sympathetic nature; I should have known better though, he's an accountant. Most of the other guys present had no such fear, they were pretty well first picks every week, the ones yet to arrive were the reserves so to speak. Rob looked back at the sheet of paper he'd scribbled the predicted side on the night before, when not expecting quite so many to turn up. As usual this had taken him two minutes flat, the team picked itself when the same nine faces showed up every Saturday with a couple or three in addition, alternating from week to week.

My pathetic expression paid dividends as I crept apologetically onto the subs bench alongside Clem, Darren and Richard Taylor. Two of the guys yet to turn up found their plans for the start of the weekend were to change, Rob deciding bad news was best delivered by mobile phone rather than face to face. I'd have done the same.

Six or seven cars made the forty minute journey to Stourbridge, Clem sharing my car and having a stab at setting up my Christmas present, a satellite navigation system, as we travelled. As he tapped away at it, my mobile phone rang and I switched on the car speaker phone, it was Kate.

"Hello Mrs, don't say anything nasty about Clem, he's sat right next to me," I hastily replied before she said anything for my ears only.

"Well I'm glad you're sitting down. You've had another speeding ticket".

"What? I've only just had one!"

"Well this is another. It's from Dumfries & Galloway, you were doing 91 in a 70, must have been when we came back from your Dad's," she said calmly.

"But I'm on 6 points already with that last one. 91 in a 70? That could be a six pointer, I could be banned."

My mind sped down the track. A ban meant no driving, no driving meant no job, I was no good to a company as salesman if I couldn't leave my front door, not many customers lay on the 359 bus route from Aldridge to Birmingham. Kate and I mused over the possibilities; three points and a £60 fine? Six points and a big fine? Banned for one month? Two months? Three? This could be serious, it was pretty worrying. We said our farewells as I reduced my speed on the M5 to a more sensible level, talk about shutting the stable door after the horse had bolted.

South Road is your stereo-typical WMCFL venue in that the changing rooms are heavily graffitied, padlocked brick buildings with toilets you could do a number 1 in, but you wouldn't dream of engaging your rear end over. It boasts two pitches, both of which are slightly sloped with grass marginally beating bare ground for elbow room. Both pitches have a road running along one side that a hefty clearance would reach if the heavily branched trees didn't intervene, and both have a dramatically sloped bank just ten feet from the opposite touchline which was the bane of every substitutes life. A ball didn't have to leave the playing surface by far before it disappeared fifty yards down the steep bank, sub's making chase while a spare ball was handed to the throw-in taker. It could be a humbling experience, fetching a discarded ball while the players continued their game with another one, like you were picking up someone's litter.

A heavy night of rain left the pitch soggy but no puddles had formed and the game was definitely on. Chawn Hill's players were putting up the nets as we walked by towards the dressing rooms, they seemed pretty chirpy about life, probably expecting a comfortable home victory against lower league opposition and rightly so, they were the league champions after all. In truth though, our league being a very even one in terms of quality, there weren't any grounds for their complacency and their confidence would carry no weight with us anyway, most of our players weren't close followers of league tables nor other teams form, they simply turned up and played, the name of the opposition didn't matter. The fact that today's opponents were last year's league champions was completely lost on them and this was no bad thing otherwise a needless inferiority complex may have set in.

The St Thomas squad of fifteen sat down in the changing rooms, Rob plonking the kit bag in the middle, and the scrummage began for the best pair of socks and least unflattering shorts. Numbered shirts mattered to a handful of them too, Pig, also known as Piggy, grabbed number 4, his Gerrard shirt. Mark Hadden, recent acquisition from now defunct Grenfell, sought the number 9 shirt and with good reason since he'd scored two hat-tricks in recent weeks. Matt Brady, tall chap with a physique that must have cost him three hours a day in a gymnasium for the last three years, donned number 8. The rest of the players didn't seem too fussed what number they wore as long as it was no higher than 11. The banter kept coming, the spirit seemed good.

Before we left the dressing room, Rob Hill read from a script that all managers had been given at the previous week's league meeting. We pinned back our ears to listen as he delivered it in earnest -

'Gentlemen,' it began, *'because after all we are all gentlemen. It has come to my attention more and more as this season has progressed that the standard of behaviour towards match officials have reached unacceptable levels and it is with regret that I have to remind you all of the WMCFL mission statement. I'd hoped this would not be neccessary but the amount of abuse the league's referees have had to face simply will no longer be tolerated so I will repeat the committee's stand on behaviour.'* It went on to explain how one referee had resigned, and others had passed comment upon the abuse they had been receiving from spectators, substitutes and to a lesser extent, players. We were reminded that this was a Christian league which stood for certain values and persistent abuse of the referee did not sit amongst those values. It was fair comment and received in the right manner despite the

occasional interruption where ludicrous refereeing decisions were dragged up from the past. Sure enough, the league's referees were far from great but ask any club at any level whether they thought the refs were good and the answer would likely be the same – no. Missive read and duly noted, it was on to business.

Without being unkind to the referee today, he didn't exactly look the part. He'd opted for spongy souled running shoes rather than football boots for some reason and on this muddy pitch they were doomed to failure on two counts, first he'd slip around like an ice skater and second, they wouldn't stay a gleaming bright powder blue for very long. His black socks were ill fitting to put it politely, ending their trail mid-shin, and the navy blue knee support looked a bit silly a few inches beneath his white tennis shorts. He had a proper black referee's top on but this was discarded within five minutes when he realised it clashed with Chawn Hill's dark blue shirts so to complete the dishevelled look, he borrowed a two sizes too big sky blue hooded tracksuit top with 'GAP' emblazoned across the front. The messy overlong grey hair waved in the wind atop his fifty odd year old head making him look less like a referee and more like a mad professor carrying a whistle while out for a jog.

Within ten minutes it should have been 3-0 to the home team. They knew this pitch well and opted to kick downhill first half to take advantage of the slope and following wind. Three times they sent a high ball over the top of our defence and three times their striker fluffed his opportunity with only the keeper to beat, once hilariously by missing the bouncing ball altogether before tumbling unchallenged in a heap on the turf. I looked on expecting an embarrassed grin or hand warming beamer from him but he trotted back blank faced, hoping no-one had noticed. Believe me we had noticed on the substitutes bench and he received pelters when running onto any through ball for the remainder of the half.

A couple more opportunities were missed by Chawn Hill before half time while we rarely troubled their keeper. The game was being played in a light drizzle which clung to those of us on the sidelines like cold cling film, but the players were having a wonderful time, slide tackling at every opportunity, careful to ensure the ball, man and kitchen sink were taken out of play. The St Thomas players gathered by the touchline at the half-time whistle, guzzling water from plastic bottles while Chawn Hill disappeared into the dressing room for their half time de-brief, well most of them did, I counted three stood outside taking the opportunity to have a smoke. Rob rightly saw no need to alter the side at the break, leaving the four subs to get that little bit colder on the sidelines, but by now we were each resigned to our fate and were happy to shout and holler our encouragement to the team as the second half proceeded. In the event, Clem came on for the last 20 minutes and Rich Taylor for the last fifteen, both in midfield where fresh legs were needed. Rob kindly apologised for not putting me on and I thanked him for having the good grace not to. I can only play in defence and it would have been a thankless task being chucked on for the last ten minutes when the only genuine mark you could make on the match would be that of a mistake. "But you told me you could change a game Alex," he said. "Yeah, but I didn't tell you which way," I replied.

And then, on 85 minutes, after Chawn Hill had passed up a couple more scoring chances, a St Thomas attack saw the ball fall at the feet of Chris Preece, our central defender still in the opposition box because he was too knackered to trot back to his position after a corner. He was ten yards from goal and without enough time to think or panic, he slotted the ball through a forest of legs and into the corner of the net. 1-0! Thankyou very much and good night. You got the feeling Chawn Hill hadn't factored in the possibility of going behind, and now that they had, they realised there wasn't sufficient time to do anything about it. They huffed and puffed their way upfield a couple of more times but the stuffing had been knocked out of them and as the referee blew the final whistle, his blue running shoes now muddy brown and his hooded top covering up his shorts making him look like he was wearing a dress, they were left to rue the first half misses that may have put the game beyond doubt. St Thomas' players cavorted, the substitutes applauded, Chawn Hill aborted. Victory for St Thomas, the cup was still within grasp!

CHAPTER SIX

"... don't look back on an empty feeling..."

'Match off, waterlogged pitch,' read Rob's text message on a Thursday afternoon. How the groundsman had managed to take this decision 48 hours ahead of kick-off was beyond us, particularly as the weather had improved since a downpour the previous night which must have brought on his knee jerk reaction. I was disappointed, but not as much as Steve Busby who I'd bumped into while he was jogging earlier that day, he'd never have done any form of preparatory exercise if he knew the match was gonna be off.

The cancellation left me in a quandry. I'd been invited to Old Trafford to see Villa play Man United the same afternoon as the St Thomas match. No ordinary match ticket mind, it was the full corporate entertainment package including meeting players of yesteryear, scoffing a three course meal and drinking as much as you could, free gratis. It was the 'as much as you could drink' part that was causing me consternation and rendering my attendance unlikely. I'd declined the invitation initially, believing there was insufficient time for me to leave Aldridge having played a game of football and reach Manchester in time for the pre-match nosebag. Now the St Thomas game was off the agenda, I had oodles of time to drive to Manchester but still felt uneasy about doing so.

"People and places," Peter had pounded into me from the moment I first started seeing him over my alcoholism. "Be careful who you're spending your time with and where you're spending it, a bad combination and you'll be in danger." Almost three years ago he'd told me that, well two years, ten months and six days to be exact, not that I was counting. The advice had held me in very good stead during several rocky periods and I realised it needed heeding once again, despite it being at the cost of an all expenses paid trip to Britain's most famous stadium to see my favourite team play, or more accurately, get gubbed. I was disappointed but knew it made sense, and my brother Stuart understood my decision although he'd be sorry to be going without me.

Our Aunty had secured the four tickets from a supplier to her business and since she had no interest in football, she'd kindly passed them on to my brother Stuart, her son John, his friend and me. I'd been a supporter of Villa since I was old enough for my Dad to tell me I was one, thirty years or so now, and the opportunity to see them play at Manchester United was not something I passed up lightly, but ask any recovering alcoholic serious about his or her sobriety and they'll say you must never get complacent. It doesn't matter how long you've gone without a drink, each day is the first. It seemed far from sensible then to spend my Saturday afternoon participating in an all expenses paid jolly to Old Trafford and watch people around me guzzling lager as if it were about to be outlawed.

I remember Peter telling me a story about his friend Jim, a regular at the Alcohol Misuse Group he attended in Telford. Jim was in his fifties and had gone eleven years without so much as a sniff of a drink after coming close to death through many years of drinking. He'd turned his life around after a messy divorce which had left him with little money and few friends, and his daughters had had nothing to do with him for a long time. Gradually, over his eleven years without alcohol, fences were mended with family and friends and he'd become able to hold down a full time job, earning enough to keep his new wife and himself in relative comfort. Previously he'd been a company director with the salary and bonuses to match, but these days he lived rather more humbly, but with much more peace in his soul now he'd managed to beat the demon drink.

One Sunday, his wife was making dinner. The recipe required a small amount of stout so she'd bought one of those tiny tins of Mackeson stout, about half the size of a regular can of coke. She poured the requisite amount into the mixture and placed the remainder on the fridge, next to where Jim was standing. Inexplicably, knowing there was barely any stout left in the tin but overlooking the gravity of his actions, Jim picked it up and poured the remaining two fingers or so into his mouth. "Might as well finish this off, won't do any harm."

Within three days he was in hospital, this sip of stout proving the catalyst to a three day bender which saw him cramming as much alcohol as he was able into his body. It was as easy as that for the pack of cards to tumble, one false move, one brief act of complacency where the eye is taken off the ball and wallop, eleven years of sobriety ended as your mind sends you back into the behaviour it had become accustomed to over all those years.

I wasn't going to take the risk of a trip to Old Trafford. I'd been in pubs very occasionally over the last three years but always at lunchtimes and making sure I was in the kind of company that I knew I wouldn't drink in front of; my children, my brother, my wife. I'd not been to a pub on an evening for ages and certainly not with friends who weren't aware of my situation, it was too dangerous. In the wrong circumstances I knew how easy it would be for me to pick up a drink again. Perversely, inexplicably, I harboured a romantic notion of how my return to drinking might occur; in a dimly lit trendy bar, young, happy faces having a good time while listening to decent music. I had a clear vision of this collapse, I'd have nightmares about it; me leaning up against the bar in animated conversation with a friend as he sipped from a pint of lager. I'd nurse my coca-cola as per usual and as I finished it, the barman would mistakenly place a pint of lager in front of me having misheard my friend's request for another round. Nonchalantly I'd pick the pint up with my right hand while leaning on the bar with my left, and without a care in the world take a sip just like the millions of other people who do so every day. People around me would be happily oblivious to the gravity of my actions, and my friend would smile with relief as he watched me drink, as if welcoming me back into the fold, our friendship blossoming as the night wore on with us both getting merrily drunk. I was back in the land of the living, of the normal.

I had my excuses ready, loads of them. I could absolve myself of responsibility since it wasn't me that ordered the drink. I could say it had been a mistake and an aberration not to be repeated (though I knew this to be folly). I could get so leathered that people would feel sorry for me when they found out what had happened. I could carry on drinking the next day and people would understand and be sympathetic because I had an illness. It'd be a doddle being forgiven and as long as I controlled my drinking this time around, I could soon be a social drinker without people I know looking at me with their side eyes.

Sometimes I yearned to drink again. Over the near three years of my recovery, I'd spent the first six months getting by on sheer willpower, the next eighteen months having adapted comfortably to my new life, but the last ten months resenting every minute of it. I was feeling vulnerable because I'd found myself resisting alcohol not for myself but for others, and when you get to that stage it becomes very difficult. The reason I'd not taken a drink in recent months wasn't because I knew what a disaster it would be for myself, but because I couldn't put my close family and Peter through the trauma of seeing me return to drinking, it would cripple them and strain our relationships surely to breaking point. So I reluctantly turned down the Man United jolly, my defences were already shaky and I didn't need pushing over the edge by an innocent group of good time charlies on a boozy away day. Had it been just Stuart and me I'd have stood a chance but knowing John's friend and his penchant for getting bladdered at every available opportunity, I made arrangements to stay at home and watch Villa's capitulation on Sky Sports from the comfort of my armchair. But the vulnerability I was now experiencing after a long time sober was beginning to trouble me.

My drinking started at fifteen. I lived in a small coastal town fifteen miles south of Aberdeen with my parents and two younger brothers. The town of Stonehaven housed nine thousand people and boasted regular amenities that a boy of fifteen wasn't interested in; library, bowling green and such like. Looking back it also had plenty else on offer that I could and should have taken advantage of instead of drinking; tennis courts, swimming pool, a golf course and a picturesque harbour that my youngest brother explored in depth 'till the late hours. But these were only practical for six months of the year when it was light and warm enough to take part, October to March was a different matter when you were rising in the dark and returning home from school in the dark. Options became limited.

Entrenched in middle class, we were your standard family of working parents and pleasant, dutiful sons. None of us were rebels, Chris had his moments but never of grievous intent, only the playful hi-jinks of a ten year old, although inadvertently setting fire to his bedroom caused a scare or two. The three of us behaved at school, were pleasant to people and wrote thank you cards to our Granny's for their birthday presents. Dad worked at a bank, Mum was a health visitor, we were by no means a dysfunctional family. Yet in my boredom I was introduced to alcohol by friends of my age attempting to be adults and it was downhill from there.

I remember vividly my first drink. I was alone, locked in the bathroom of our house one summer's evening. My parents were out and I was worried that they might return unexpectedly, so I hid. I was fifteen but looked younger. I had no hope of buying alcohol over the counter at the off licence, so a friend obtained a couple of bottles of Pils for me. "Take these to the party Russon, we'll have two each," he'd said, giving them to me as a safety measure in case his own parents found them about his person. He hadn't intended for me to crack one open but I took this precaution rather than embarrass myself in front of my peers at the party. I'd feel a fool if I gurned and choked at the first intake of alcohol, I wanted to know what to expect. I remember it taking me an age to get the bottle top off, I'd not done it before. My index finger was red raw from aborted attempts with the bottle opener, but I managed to fiddle the cap off in the end and spilt a puddle of lager on the bathroom carpet in the process, it gave off a strong stench that didn't appeal. I took my first swig, it tasted horrible, Pils not being a standard strength lager but a strong one, not that I knew this at the time, the taste was like nothing I'd ever experienced. I'd naively expected something along the lines of the Shandy Bass I enjoyed at Christmas time, a sweet taste not sour. Nevertheless I stuck to my task and grimly downed half a bottle of the stuff before pouring the remainder down the toilet when I could take no more. The effect was instant, half a bottle of strong lager on a first timer of a fifteen year old who hadn't eaten since breakfast, was enough to have me staggering around the bathroom. I remember feeling tremendous, I was unsteady on my feet and smiling all over my face as I struggled to stand in front of the mirror. So this was what alcohol did to you, this was why all those drinkers on telly would stumble around and slur their words. This was cool, I liked it. Not the taste, I hated that, but the effect. The sun shone brightly though the frosted bathroom window on an immature fifteen year old boy, about to meet his friends at the bus station for a ride to Newtonhill and a Summer's evening fayre where he hoped to get off with Claire Harrison, and now he was full of dutch courage, he fancied his chances. I clearly remember that momentous occasion, not getting off with Claire Harrison because it never happened, but standing in that bathroom regarding myself in the mirror and sensing I'd discovered something here that was the key to a happier life.

With the Saturday morning match against Rowley cancelled, a training session was organised instead. A chance to have a kick around rather than skulk around shops or lie in bed. Bizzarely, the venue was to be our home ground, the very place deemed unplayable two days prior, and when we alighted and took a look at the pitch it confirmed our belief that the game should never have been called off at all. There'd been not a drop of rain since the hasty cancellation and the playing conditions were perfect for amateur football, damp under foot and a blustery wind to cause mayhem in defence. Hmm, perhaps it was best it'd been called off after all, there speaks a defender.

I don't consider myself as someone who excels in many things in life but punctuality is one, I'm hardly ever late. Regardless of the occasion, significant or otherwise, I'll be there at the appointed hour, well five minutes early to make sure in most circumstances. Today was no different as I pulled my car up at the Stick & Wicket, thankfully alongside plenty of others. I'd been to an aborted training session just before Christmas to find only two others present and feared the same may occur, but a four game unbeaten streak had apparently revived the troops' dedication to the team and training would be well attended. That's until I realised there were actually only two of our guys present, the remaining cars belonged to parents of the under 12's club kicking around on the far pitch.

I stood about in the car park with Chas, our keeper Rob and his teenage son Tom. Their attire told me they'd been here before, they wore jeans and casual clothes while I stood shivering in football shorts, training top, all the gear ready to go. It seemed clear to me that the three of them fully expected to remain in their snug clothing and not have to change, they seemed confident that too few players would turn up to make a training session worthwhile. Matt pulled up his collar and dug his hands into his pockets, Rob and Tom clambered back into the warmth of their car, I hopped from foot to foot with the wind whipping around my legs. Perhaps I should have stayed at home.

Yet one by one the stragglers emerged until we had enough for a six-a-side. Richard Taylor arrived on his mountain bike having been drenched by a short downpour. Pig, dressed like an eskimo in a bright red bobble hat and enough padding to see him through the winter, had decided to run here, the rest of them arrived by car. You can sometimes guess a person's profession by the car they drive. I'd not had the opportunity to find much out about my new team mates so had no idea what they did to earn a living, their cars were all I had to go on. Chas I'd decided was a painter and decorator, he had a maroon Ford Escort estate of a certain vintage which he hadn't taken the trouble to show a shammy in quite a while. Chris Preece, our lanky central defender with longish hair dangling down in front of his face requiring him to part it with both hands like a pair of curtains, was in computers I deduced judging by the nippy black Peugot gleaming clean despite the dreary weather we'd had. Then the familiar sight of Clem's metallic silver Golf pulled up as a reminder to me that judging a bloke's profession by his car was riduculous. School teachers drove Skodas surely?

If we're honest, footballers at our standard would confess to having mixed feelings on a cold, winter's morning as more and more players gradually turn up for training. When you're standing shivering in a car park and the agreed start time comes and goes with only three or four having turned up, your eyes light up as you start to contemplate the training session being called off. Your warm home beckons, perhaps a return to bed or the cosy thought of the weekend newspapers spread out on your kitchen table. The disappointment of a cancelled game of footie is brief, you begin to hope no more players turn up. Then one more arrives; not to worry there's still not enough to make a training session viable. Then another; nah, you can't play 3-a-side. When you get to eight attendees though it starts to dawn on you that this is probably going to go ahead. You swap hopeful glances, enquiring of each other's interest in this training session, but then someone else arrives, then another, and the warmth of your car is soon banished from your thoughts.

So, after conversations were exchanged about how bladdered people had got the night before and how ludicrous it was that the game had been called off, we set off on a cross country run led by the ever vibrant Pig, who soon extended a fifty yard advantage over us. We ran about a mile and by the finish were strung out like washing on a line, Buzz and Preece bringing up the rear as they laughed and joked about the previous night's caperings. Buzz wasn't laughing for long, he spent the rest of the training session complaining of jogger's nipple which he used as an excuse for his lame performance. Stuart Pearce once famously played on for West Ham despite carrying a broken leg, we didn't have too much sympathy then for Buzz's chafed nipples.

No stretches, we were straight into a six-a-side match on a patch of grass away from the match pitch, where the groundsman hopefully wouldn't mind us playing. The rain was steadily drenching us now, our shirts clinging to the skin and hair matted to our heads. The increasingly sterner wind raged across our makeshift pitch with jumpers for posts. Fluorescent yellow bibs were handed out to six players who now looked like they should be digging the roads or helping children across them, and the game began. Six-a-sides never have a formal centre circle kick-off, they commence with an impatient player drop kicking the ball into the sky and shouting, "It's off!" The teams looked hopelessly unfair. Six regular first teamers wearing yellow with an assortment of substitutes and part-timers for their opposition, of which I was one. We did have one regular player on our side, Rob the keeper, who seized his opportunity to free himself of the goalkeeping shackles and announced he was playing 'out'. We were playing rush keepers but he wasn't even prepared to be that, he was like a bird freed from a cage as he pranced around the pitch as far as possible from his customary home of the six yard box. Keepers always think they make excellent outfield players, they're frustrated midfield generals, desperate to parade their ball skills when given the chance, although they've no more skill with a football than I have in the kitchen. They are to outfield football what Girls Aloud are to indie music, a hopeless mismatch. However, they won't be told, so Rob raced away with the ball every time he found it at his feet, taking on allcomers. Each time he attempted to dribble past an opponent, the same result ensued, his opponent sticking out a leisurely leg and tackling him without fuss. Half an hour later, when finally accepting the dribbling wasn't coming off, Rob resorted to a Tony Daley style of beating the defender – hoof it past him then beat him for pace. Unfortunately our erstwhile keeper is 42 years old and with the best will in the world, he is not going to beat a triathlete like Clem over a fifty yard dash.

Rich Taylor was on our side, the only bloke to have turned up today looking like he meant business. His attire was that of a proper footballer; white Adidas football shorts, white knee length football socks with three red hoops folded over below the knee, a black Adidas drill top and a clean pair of football boots. The rest of us appeared to have dragged on the first items we'd found in the dirty washing that looked vaguely sporty, baggy jogging bottoms and creased tracksuit tops abounded as did a selection of dodgy headgear. I was the worst culprit turning out as I had in a Teenage Fanclub tour t-shirt and a St Andrews golf course bobble hat. That said, I found myself playing the most impressive training session I could remember. My every touch either brought the ball instantly under control or delivered it to a team-mate's feet and I was feeling quite chipper about myself. I'm by no means a skilful footballer but today everything was coming off and I found myself trotting around with my shoulders squared and my chest puffed out Cantona style. For once I had earned the right to be on a football pitch, albeit a makeshift six-a-side pitch out of sight in the corner of a hockey arena with at least five serious hangovers ambling around me, but I was playing decent football nonetheless. Then I let myself down and crashed back to earth.

Ian Pearsall, not a man I'd choose to mess with, had brought along a friend called Glynn. He was a shortish kind of chap, didn't look much like a footballer but fancied a run around. He was on the opposition's right wing and called for a pass from defence which was duly delivered by Pig. The pass was fired at pace for him to run on to and the moment it was delivered, I sensed I could intercept it. In this judgement I turned out to be wrong. Arriving at full speed to slide the ball away from Glynn, I found upon my arrival that he had managed to nudge it forward out of my reach, but it was too late for me to halt my advance. My momentum carried me forward as I stretched out my right leg to slide tackle him and I crashed into the poor guy, somersaulting him on impact and he landed in an unceremonious heap upon me as I lay prostrate on the floor.

"F***in' hell geez, what was that?" exclaimed Mr Pearsall, "It's only f***in' trainin'."

"Cool the f***in' beans," offered Pig, "F***in' 'ell."

Further comments and murmurings in support of Pig and Pearsall's protestations were put forward by others as I sheepishly rose to my feet. In the guide book 'How To Win Friends & Influence People' I don't remember a chapter on butchering a good friend of your new team-mates in training. It reminded me of a similar incident when I'd joined St Mary's; I'd deposited Phil Kinson onto his backside within seconds of him taking part in his first ever training session having been brought along as a friend of the manager, now I was doing it again.

I tried to defend my actions by claiming a tackle with fair intentions, which it was, but this cut no ice with anyone and I was rightly reminded that had I performed this assault on a matchday there'd have been no complaints, but taking a friend of theirs to the cleaners as he trod gingerly in an attempt to rid himself of a hangover was simply not cricket. I agreed and slunk back into goal to take my turn as rush keeper.

We played for about an hour before fatigue, disinterest and rain called a halt to proceedings. I felt I'd done enough by the finish to atone for my tackle by having quiet words of apology with Glynn and his mate Ian, but amends were fully made in the eyes of everybody when Clem took the trouble, with only two minutes remaining, to crunch into me and leave me on the deck clutching a throbbing shinpad-less shin. A cheer went up, retribution had been delivered and Glynn had the biggest smile.

CHAPTER SEVEN

"... and it's no good, it's no good, it's no good..."

If I had a major fault, and there are many to choose from, my judgmental nature would probably beat my impatience by a short head. Despite being as long a distance from the perfect human being as you could hope to be, I somehow find it within myself to judge others, and more often than not, I choose to measure their shortcomings rather than their virtues. It's not a trait I'm proud of, I pray regularly for God's grace to help me remove it from my make up, but for now it remains and as a result it was the turn tonight of Gary Lineker, Match Of The Day's frontman, to feel the benefit of my opinion. I needed to get my feelings about the man off my chest and found the forum to release my frustration on Heroes & Villains message board, a place I regularly unburden my mind onto. It read as follows -

"I know he's the blue eyed boy, was never booked as a player (well maybe once) and is the housewife's pin-up, but can somebody tell me who told Gary Lineker he should go into TV presenting? It's getting too much. If my toes curl any further they're going to break. The stilted intros, awkward exchanges, lame asides, I just can't take it anymore. It's like watching your Dad on the dancefloor. I'm sure he's a lovely bloke, a fine upstanding citizen and you can't knock his footballing career but honestly, he's taken to television presenting like a duck to treacle. He's like a rabbit caught in a car's headlights when he stares at the camera, trying to look relaxed but appearing to have just filled his pants, he looks like a paralysed Alan Partridge. To witness his exchanges with Shearer is to see desperation at work. Lineker, bent forward over the desk, offering an asinine question that can only be returned with a statement of the bleeding obvious which Shearer, his hair desperately arranged to suggest he's not going bald, delivers with aplomb. The two of them continue for several minutes, saying nothing in particular, their faces gleaming with BBC make-up, their chat uniquely devoid of value, interest or meaning. And then Lawrenson pipes up from the corner of your TV set and before you know it we have the matey threesome guffawing in unison, Lawro nestling into his role of ex-pro, delivering all the lines we've heard a thousand times before."

I feel like the walls are closing in on me, I shrink with despair. This weekly old pals act wearing me down like a George Bush monologue. It's too much, I turn the sound down and wait for the next match, but still I have to look at them. The screen lurches between Shearer's front row, he must share dentists with Dennis Waterman, Lawro's greying centre parting, his hair taller than a block of flats, and Lineker's entire chest revealed to the world by the lowest open necked shirt in history. They babble on then finally it's the football. Oh great, Man United v Villa is first up, another defeat. Telly off, time for bed.

Adam, a friend of my brother's, put it perfectly when he said these three needed to be split up, rather like naughty schoolboys who act the giddy goat together in class. They need to be put in different classrooms for their own good and those around them, or better still, the studio of a Danish football programme shown in the middle of the night on a satellite channel I'll never know the number of.

My Christmas present from Santa, a satellite navigation system, was going down a treat. I'd railed against these gizmos for a long time, I had maps and a road atlas, why the need to be spoonfed directions when I'm trying to listen to my stereo? Finally, however, I'd relented when a colleague drove me to a business meeting in the depths of Cheltenham guided by his sat nav and I saw first hand just what a piece of cake satellite navigation made getting from A to B. I shared my excitement with Santa, told him I'd been largely good this year, and he duly rewarded me with a Tom Tom.

If you've got a satellite navigation system you'll know that a voice directs you to where you want to go after you've typed in the address, simple. You can choose from a selection of voices and languages, female or male. I went one better when Clem managed to download an alternative voice off the internet – the chap off Phoenix Nights who has his face painted for an Open Day but can't wash it off again, can't remember his name but I do remember he spent the rest of the series with his face looking like a cat's.

So with our match today being away at a ground I'd never visited before, I engaged the help of Phoenix Nights as I plotted my way to Amblecote with two younger members of the team as passengers,

Podge and Athers. They're early twenties at a guess and driving them the forty minute journey from our Anchor Meadow starting point, I soon sensed the age gap.

"Sorry lads, you'll have to put up with the music of an older man today, fancy some Bob Dylan?" I ventured. They looked at each other with furrowed brow, who was Bob Dylan?

"Or I've got The Smiths, Teenage Fanclub, take your pick." More furrowed brows.

"Anything mate," came the reply, "Not fussed really."

I plumped for Kings Of Leon thinking this might suggest I was down with the kids, but this too appeared to pass them by. I figured we came from different eras and settled back to listen to the music alone while they laid plans for their afternoon following the football. Podge was fitting Athers' laminate flooring it transpired and a suitable commencement time was to be negotiated.

Rob Hill didn't meet us at Anchor Meadow, he was sat at home, knee to toe in plaster after an achilles operation earlier in the week. Steve Busby arrived to confirm there were enough players to make a team before wagons rolled. Rob hoped to be driven to the game later by his good lady wife if the weather didn't worsen. It had been a stormy week with high winds causing havoc across the country, several people losing their lives due to falling walls, trees and scaffolding. It put my flattened fence panel into perspective.

The team missed Rob. We travelled to the game and prepared for the game in Amblecote's away dressing room, surely the smartest in the league. Spacious, clean, a large showering area, it even had lockers. Without Rob present though, to organise us and kick our arses into shape, the fourteen of us drifted around the changing rooms in no apparent hurry to reach the pitch in time for kick-off. Men are like a bunch of schoolkids when you get them into a football environment. Fully employed, mortgage paying grown men, some with children, some leaders of men at their place of work, seem to leave their responsible personas behind once around a football club and become quiet and sheepish, afraid to put themselves forward. I'm as bad as anyone. So while the three match officials, all kitted up and waiting outside our dressing room for the teamsheet, kicked their heels with impatience, we continued to drift around the place without a care in the world. And we were only five minutes from kick-off. Instead of being out on the pitch, stretching our muscles, jogging out tense limbs or getting a feel for the ball, we were still bouncing to gangsta rap while only half dressed. I meekly suggested to the lads that it was perhaps about time we made our way to the pitch, so did one or two others, but without Rob there to literally push us out of the dressing room there was nobody taking charge. And why should they? You'd think fourteen hairy arsed blokes could individually manage to organise themselves sufficiently to alight at a given football pitch at a given time, but not without their manager they couldn't. Thankfully the referee showed leniency and after heaving us out of the dressing room, allowed the game to kick off ten minutes late with our right winger still pulling on his shirt as the game commenced.

This was a cup match, the last in a round robin format with lots of permutations possible as to which two of the five teams in our mini-league would progress. We knew where we stood, anything other than a victory would see us out, and we were playing the league leaders away from home, not an enticing prospect but ours being the sort of league where virtually any team can beat any other, there was no need for panic. Well not collective panic, I allowed myself slight palpitations when learning I was to play left back against the league's leading goalscorer.

It's not often we play with a full complement of match officials but now and again we receive the 'benefit' of two linesmen and today was to be one such occasion. This became significant as the game progressed. Linesmen in our league are referees in their own right but are asked occasionally to double as 'lino's or as they'd have it these days, referee's assistants. Resplendent in full black kit, the three officials made a striking change from the character we'd had at Chawn Hill two weeks ago who'd officiated while looking like Frank Bough in a gym kit. We felt honoured. A full set of officials and playing on a flat pitch with, get this, a dugout! Yes, a proper sit on the bench, protected from the wind, dugout. We'd hit the big time and just needed a performance to match to progress into the quarter finals of the cup.

The master plan upon winning the toss was for us to kick with the aid of a gusty following wind and make our opponents play against the bright sun set low in the sky behind our goal. This two pronged advantage would surely find Amblecote on the back foot while we rained shots down on their goal. In the event however, the ball remained for the most part in our half with wave after wave of attack being repelled by last ditch tackles, misplaced final balls or the seizure of the ball by an angry gust of wind, taking it away from it's intended target. We rode it out for a good half hour until all our hard work was undone by a hesitation between centre back and keeper with a heavy emphasis of blame lying on the keeper. While Joe and keeper Rob gave it the 'you have it, no you have it' routine, gazing at a long through ball and waiting for each other to take charge of the situation, Ambelecote's bald headed striker sprinted in to intercept and score. It was the sort of goal you've seen a thousand times before but feel helpless to do anything about as you look on waiting for the car crash to happen, I was just relieved that for once I wasn't at the heart of the muck-up.

We not only managed to recover after a brief period licking our wounds, but even had the cheek to equalise when Nick Jones shuffled down the right wing, turned the ball onto his left foot, and lofted the ball into the top corner from the edge of the box. A fantastic goal not matched by his goalscoring celebration, he simply stood in shock, sharing the bewilderment of his team-mates. He'd used his left foot for something other than standing on for the first time in three seasons. The remainder of the first half was played out with a flurry of Amblecote corners giving us the willies, each one hanging in the wind before falling underneath our crossbar for Rob to punch away. A couple of others I nodded away powerfully and with great encouragement from my team-mates who were still trying to suss out whether this Russon guy was any good or not. They'd seen me play well once in training, and averagely in a friendly, but were understandably circumspect when deliberating over whether they should pass the ball to me or not. I was circumspect too, when the ball's passed to you and you find yourself under instant pressure from your opposite number, it's easy to get flustered and be dispossessed, much easier instead to hide from the ball so it can't be passed to you. You can't make a mistake then. In this game though I decided to put my head above the parapet a little more and regularly found the ball at my feet, occasionally passing it to a man in space but mostly hoofing it aimlessly forward, accepted behaviour when you're a defender, no frills, just lump it away from the danger area. I'd put in a couple of good challenges to prevent strikers advancing on goal and all in all was delighted with my first half showing as the referee blew for half-time with the scores level, already I felt my performance was good enough to cement my place for the following weekend's fixture. I hadn't however reckoned on my second half offering…

The half-time interval saw us slapping one another on the back in congratulation of a good half, until Joe piped up with the memorable line "Let's not lick each other's arses yet boys, there's forty five minutes to go." Never have I heard a better worded plea against complacency. He was of course correct to bring our attention to matters in hand rather than matters past. Though we'd acquitted ourselves well, we weren't leading and had the troublesome wind and sun to face in the second half. Rob Hill had arrived by now, on his crutches, keeping his distance from the half-time de-brief not having seen much of the opening half, except Nick's goal and our backs to the wall finish. He pulled his coat collar up and nestled his chin into it, crossing his arms and legs to try and hunch some warmth back into his cold body. He rather looked the part, a proper manager in a proper dugout, holding a clipboard with the team sheet on it, instructing his substitutes to warm up and having a word with the linesman as he retook his position for the resumption of the game. The wind strengthened as our seventeen stoner of a referee blasted his whistle and we were away again.

The wheels began to fall off from the moment I goofed a clearance a minute into the second half. A routine through ball to their centre forward should have been comfortably dealt with by my size tens but instead, I delivered a spectacular fresh air shot while sliding to the turf and Shawn Devenport was through on goal with just the keeper to beat. It was kind of him to screw his shot wide but this spared my blushes only temporarily, there were more blunders to come. Having dusted myself down I followed up this bloomer with a couple of ineffectual tackles and a missed header which sailed over my head as I misjudged it spectacularly. My luck ran out when a midfielder burst through to skin me alive and cross for their striker to put them 2-1 up. Sixty five minutes had gone, and when I looked across at the touchline to see Podge warming up in earnest, I feared my substitution was in the offing. As a team we'd failed to perform in the second half and fallen a goal behind after a good Amblecote move, and with the captain weighing up the changes, I'd put myself in pole position for a substitution with my twenty minute patch of pity. I could have no arguments when I was hauled off moments later, Podge replacing me at left back.

When you stand on the sidelines and watch a game you've been involved in, surprise and regret strike you in equal measure. Surprise that the game is so much slower than you thought, with acres of space to control and deliver the ball accurately, and regret that you didn't acknowledge this while you were on the pitch. I'd become caught up in the hurly burly of a game that in truth was being played at a fairly pedestrian pace, I just didn't know it. I watched players on both sides panicked into long clearances when they had time to drink a cup of tea before an opposing player closed them down. I made a mental note to remember this when next I turned out, hopefully next weekend, and looked on as we searched for another equaliser. It didn't come, and looked an even more remote possibility on 70 minutes when the talking point of the match reared it's ugly head.

Ian Pearsall, our right sided midfielder, a great player and fine striker of the ball, one of life's survivors from the school of hard knocks, became somewhat infuriated when the referee awarded us a free kick on the edge of the box when our player had seemingly been fouled inside the penalty area. He remonstrated with the ref, who wasn't for budging, and after a heated exchange stepped up to clobber a pretty poor free kick into the defensive wall and away to safety. A mixture of anger with the ref's decision and frustration with himself for poxing up the free kick, saw his gasket fit to blow and those who knew him stood anxiously on the touchline fearful that a walking volcano was about to erupt. A few seconds later, it did. Ian lost possession tamely and took the trouble to take the linesman to task for not having the courage to flag for the penalty a couple of minutes prior. With the linesman rejecting his protestations, and I'm being as polite as I can here, Ian suggested that perhaps he'd like to reconsider his position as a football match official and that there was a place where the sun didn't shine that he might like to put his flag since he was apparently incapable of putting it to better use. This in itself was out of order, but worse was the flowery language that accompanied Ian's feelings. The referee had no alternative but to order him off after the linesman flagged for his attention to the incident and a team losing 2-1 to the league leaders now found itself with only ten men.

It had been a protracted ordering off and one that Ian disputed long and hard, our concentration wavering as a result, and with Ian barely having time to reach his seat in the dugout, an Amblecote attack found us 3-1 down. That was it from our point of view, our heads went down, the game was over and the only question now was how heavy the defeat was going to be.

4-1 was the answer and we couldn't leave Amblecote quick enough. The defeat was disappointing but more so the manner of the game's ending with ten men flailing like a punch drunk boxer waiting for the referee to stop the fight. This wasn't due to a lack of commitment but more an overriding shame at what the game had become with Ian's regrettable sending off. He couldn't be more apologetic afterwards and I felt for him. We all have our shortcomings and failings, mine being an addiction to alcohol before I start on my judgemental nature, Ian's is a violent short temper. It was doubtful he'd play again for St Thomas after this and we'd be the worse for his absence, he being such a good quality player, but with his dismissal coming just a fortnight after a missive from the league's committee to all club secretaries, pleading for an improvement in the treatment of officials, it seemed definite that a lengthy ban would be meted out. Watching Match Of The Day that night, El Hadj Diouf was sent off for a similar indiscretion. A club fine would be unlikely to dent his sizeable professional footballer's wallet, but Ian's likely ban I was concerned might take away much more, football, a very positive strand in his troublesome life.

CHAPTER EIGHT

"Jesus Christ is knocking at my door..."

You can't make people turn to God, they have to want it for themselves, but that doesn't stop me praying for people of no faith. I don't know the lads in the football team very well, I don't get the opportunity to get to know them really, but judging by the congregation at St Thomas on a Sunday morning and evening, I'm persuaded that very few of them feel a connection with God. I pray for each of them regularly, that should any of them be going through a difficult spell when all seems lost, that God brings someone into their lives who can point them to Him and a new beginning. That's what happened to me five years ago and my life was transformed because of it.

Before then, I had nothing but disdain for Christians. A bunch of soft, limp, do-gooders who lived under the deluded belief that an old man with a white beard sailed on the clouds and watched over them. I had a very clear picture of their laughable God, he looked around eighty years of age, had wispy grey hair that blew in the wind as he lay on a fluffy cloud in the style you would if you were lying side on to the telly, propping your head up with your hand. His body from the shoulders down was obscured by this piercingly bright white cloud and his long white beard merged into the cloud so you could barely see the join. He wasn't smiling, he had a serious face, almost a frown, and his eyes beneath bushy grey eyebrows seemed to survey all beneath him, though he never looked directly at me. I must have acquired this vision of God from RE books at school or maybe a mural on a church wall when I attended a christening as a youngster, either way it was a vivid picture of this God that I didn't believe in.

I recall my parents tinkering with church when I was around eleven years old. For a short while my two brothers and I found ourselves smartly dressed on a Sunday morning and visiting St Columbus church in Sutton Coldfield. It wasn't for long and I have virtually no memory of the experience except a pretty lame Sunday School that we were ushered out to join after fifteen minutes of the service. I never worked out what the adults did while we were making papier mache figurines of angels and Jesus. Not long after that our family moved to Stonehaven and the church thing was over. I can't ever recall conversations in our family about God, Jesus or religion and only found out in later life that my Granny was a Catholic with a firm faith. I don't blame my parents for this, most adults are oblivious to church and spirituality, looking back they were probably searching themselves at the time they found themselves frequenting St Columbus, and we as children were carried along too. I only mention it to give you an understanding that I don't come from a staunch Christian background by any means, though not an atheist one either, I simply had an utterly dormant account with God.

I was early thirties when God sent one of his messengers to pull me up by the bootstraps. I won't forget it and life has turned around from there. Alcohol and depression remain daily battles but I can cope with that now, I have a loving God to support me, but you mustn't get the impression it's easy being a Christian. Many is the time you ask God just what the heck He's playing at when you see starvation and hunger in the world and that's before you bring your own tales of woe before him. But I rest on the knowledge that God is all powerful and all knowing, and who am I to questions His methods and means for the world and it's people. Try and understand God and you've got a job on your hands, just ride with it and be thankful is my motto.

A prayer went up from me as I parted from Kate and Emily in the departure lounge cafeteria at Birmingham airport. They were flying to Aberdeen for a few days with Kate's parents while our house's windows were being replaced, it made sense them being away while a draught blew through the house and workmen clattered around the place. This was a first in many respects; Emily's first flight, Kate and my first separation of more than a few hours since getting married eighteen months ago, and my first attempt in years at living in a house alone and fending for myself. At 37 years of age you'd assume this would be a doddle but I'm hopeless when not in company for a sustained period, depression swoops in on me as I'm left to ponder my lot for too long with no-one to babble at or to remove me from my thoughts.

Kate managed to cram all of her packing into one suitcase, another first. The forecasted snow I'd assumed would see her pack a second and even third case but she'd decided to travel relatively light this time. Their boarding passes secured, Emily fed and changed, off they flew leaving me to return home in time for Arsenal v Man United on Sky. Force came round to watch it with me, his support very much with Fergie's mob but the hoodoo of my television set continued as Man United were beaten 2-1, they've never won when Force has come to mine to watch them. Must see more of him. Shortly after the game ended I received a call from Judith, Kate's Mum, to confirm they'd arrived safely and as if to prove the point, I heard Emily blarting with gusto in the background. They were in the car and on their way to Auchenblae, only forty minutes drive away.

It was going to be tough without Emily to start my day. Being an early riser, I had no problem when she stirred at 6.30 in the morning, I'd be in her bedroom like a flash to collect her from her cot. A quick nappy change as I lay her on the floor next to the nappy changing unit that had been rendered redundant from day one, then the fun would begin. But who was I going to pull silly faces at now she was in Scotland? I'd persuaded myself she liked playing peek-a-boo while I was showering, sat entranced in her bouncy chair. I loved making her giggle, sharing inanities with her while she surveyed me making breakfast and pottering around in the kitchen. She even seemed to enjoy it when I put The Charlatans on, Emily gave me so much joy that within hours of her leaving I felt pretty empty, just as I did when handing Harry and Hattie back to their Mum after I'd had my access time. Still, I consoled myself that it wouldn't be long before I'd be re-united with them. Plus Villa had ended a twelve match win-less streak yesterday so there was plenty to be happy about.

The workmen arrived the next morning to commence work on the windows. I barely had the front door open when I found myself obediently boiling the kettle for their first drink of the day. "Morning" I said. "One without and one with two sugars" came the reply with a wink. You couldn't blame them, it was freezing outside and they needed something to warm them up. We'd chosen a local firm to replace the windows, having obtained quotes from three separate sources, two local and one national. The national company we'd ruled out at a very early stage. We called them in hoping that their price would be there or thereabouts and we could employ them in the knowledge that should anything go wrong, they could be relied upon to return promptly to sort it out. In the event I regretted inviting them round at all as their salesman appeared intent on doing a number on us from the moment he walked in, pretending he'd been delayed because he'd been at a pensioner's around the corner, talking her into buying a much cheaper model than the one she'd ordered so he said.

"Mr Russon?"

"Yes that's right"

"My sincere apologies for being late. I was in fact early but took the opportunity to call in on a customer just around the corner from you. Lovely lady... .shall I take my shoes off?... .nice carpet... .but I knew she couldn't really afford the range she'd ordered so I just popped round to talk her out of it," he said breathlessly as he removed his shoes on our front doorstep. There was no need, he could have left them on.

"Not to worry," I replied, "I'm in all afternoon."

"I could have sold her the more expensive kit but I'm having a good year. I'm number 79 on the rankings and we have a thousand sales people nationwide so I don't need the higher value sale" he exclaimed proudly, "I like to treat my customers as I'd like to be treated." He stood upright giving me the opportunity to look him squarely in the eyes for the first time, and shook my hand briskly before stepping in uninvited with his truckload of folders, files, brochures and leaflets.

He was about 28 years old, well presented and slick, but too slick. Kate had joined the conversation by now and any opportunity he had to ingratiate himself to her he took, as if adhering to the greasy salesman's code for desperate window salesman. Once he got her on the subject of babies he knew he was on a winner, so I sat back silently waiting for his transparent rapport building to finish. I'm a salesman, I know the score. I was just about giving him the benefit of the doubt when he reached for his wallet to pull out a photograph of his triplets which had been left with him by his now deceased wife. My fingers reached for the back of my throat, was I expected to believe this fairytale? We went through the motions from thereon in, he measured up and gave us a quote after he'd sat us through a lengthy promotional DVD during which he managed to discredit every window company that ever existed locally. When it came to the nitty gritty of price, I took him to task over it and he started to get desperate. I can't remember the conversation verbatim but suffice to say the 'final and best price' he gave me at 4pm was bettered significantly by the time he left us at 4.15pm and even as he clambered into his car at the bottom of our drive he was hollering back at me "… remember, if you order today by 6pm using the phone number I've given you, we can discount by a further 10%… .". As it was, he turned out to be the most expensive of the three quotes but I wouldn't have given him the business if he'd been the cheapest. People buy people so the saying goes and I wasn't about to entrust four grand of my hard earned to somebody who'd tried to fleece and hoodwink me from the outset.

So it was Tony who we'd commissioned, and before he'd finished his opening cuppa of the day he was knocking seven bells out of our upstairs front window, probably in case I changed my mind all of a sudden. It's a strange sensation when you feel a stranger in your own house and that's just how I felt as the dustsheets were spread out all the way from front door to upstairs back room. I hurriedly packed my laptop away and announced to Tony that I would be gone for the day, I'd see him around 4.30pm when the dark would be closing in. He didn't even turn around to respond, he was on a mission, a wooden frame removing and glass shattering mission that needed completing before poor weather blew in. Today was cold but dry and still, if the wind and rain came he might have to down tools which would cost him money so now was no time to be exchanging pleasantries. I exited quickly…

…and where did I end up? Here, in Shrewsbury's public library where I tap away on my laptop while people sit around me in the study area trying to concentrate. The woman behind me has a text book on 'anatomy' open before her and is scribbling away furiously, she looks like a student. The man at the table in front of me, is studying a book called 'Shanties From The Seven Seas'. He too has a notepad and pen in front of him and it's intriguing me as to what he could be making notes about. Both have given me irritable looks as if to suggest the noise from my keyboard is distracting, but I can't depress the keys any quieter, and when I try I don't press them hard enough so have to keep returning to repair mis-spellings.

So why am I here? Well not because I needed somewhere to pitch my tent while Tony attacked my house, otherwise I'd have gone to a library much closer than Shrewsbury's fifty miles away, but because I've just been sent packing with my tail between my legs by a customer. I'd turned up four hours early for a 3pm appointment. I hadn't looked at my diary and arrived at completely the wrong time. I explained I'd travelled from Walsall, it had taken an hour and I had no other appointments in the area, but her response was effectively 'hard cheese' and now I have four hours to kill. The choices were as follows; spend the time at the Shrewsbury branch of the bank in an upstairs office where staff frown at you and whisper to their colleagues "Who's he?", drive back home to dial in to the bank's electronic system and keep up to date with emails, or shuffle around Shrewsbury's music shops, tea rooms and library until 3pm. I've had my coffee and bacon sandwich, bought two copies of The Wedding Present's 'George Best' album for £4.99 each (my brother wants one too) and now I'm irritating those around me in the library.

The meeting I'm about to attend is with a woman who owns a training company. She provides training courses to local government workers who need to be kept up to speed with health and safety regulations, equal opportunities and legal compliance. She charges the local councils and colleges for this service but waits many weeks for her bills to be paid, meanwhile she has bills of her own to pay, not least essentials such as wages and rents. Here I am therefore, as a representative of the bank, to offer her an advance against the unpaid bills she's waiting for her customer's to honour. Only then can she can pay her staff. We've met once before and it was frosty to say the least. Wish me luck...

...I had nothing to worry about in the event. The rigours of a working day had dulled Mrs Stourton's senses to such an extent that she was happy to keep the meeting brief and see me on my way with the documents, signed, sealed and to be delivered. I marched off to the Post

Office with a spring in my step, I've signed up around 300 business's but every one feels like the first. Explaining to her that I'd had to talk my last customer into buying for a lesser price than they'd agreed and showing her a picture of my three kids clearly worked a treat.

Conferences leave me cold, I can't imagine they leave many people much more than lukewarm, but try sitting through a banking conference and we're talking borderline refridgeration. I'm sat at the Ricoh Arena in Coventry with around 750 other delegates, colleagues, disinterested parties, call us what you will. We've drank our coffee, eaten our Danish pastries and smiled nervously for half an hour in the welcoming suite. Now we're sat ten to a round table, listening to guest speaker and facilitator for the day Trevor McDonald. He must be costing a few quid. He's applauded on stage with the sound of Stereophonics' 'Have A Nice Day' booming around the vast room.

We hadn't realised Sir Trev would be presenting today, the murmuring around the tables suggests I wasn't the only one to be cynical about his likely pay packet. We're encouraged to save costs as a company yet are happy to splash out on a famous face to lead us in corporate prayer, a man who's no more a bank person than Bernard Manning is a nun. Sir Trev gives us a short speech about the importance of teamwork and it's relevance to his life in television, explaining that he may be the front man but can only succeed if hundreds around him do their jobs right too. Fair enough if a little predictable, and then he introduces our Managing Director, Stuart Prentice, onto the stage.

Mr Prentice has dressed down for the day, I suppose to portray himself as a 'down with the people' kind of guy. But he looks a scruff with his shirt protruding below his round necked woollen sweater and above his khaki corduroys. The stage is massive, 80 feet wide, the white backdrop gleaming, the bright corporate colours spelling the toe curling strapline "Being Number One!" Toe curling turns out to be the day's theme. It's not the speaker's fault, you try making asset finance and non domestic recourse factoring sound interesting, but it's torture sitting through hours of business speak... derivatives, investment in core systems, corporate efficiencies, business strategy, yes it's all there.

One by one different speakers from the company's board of directors get to their feet and subject us to a monologue on their department's individual disciplines. They seem genuinely passionate but surely this is an act? How can a man be passionate about financial planning and intrinsic modular systems? There's so much 'them and us' about today. The 750 of us are sat at tables spread across the room while the Executive coccoon themselves within their own territory, where they can't be got at, sharing a table and congratulating each other on speeches as deliverers return to their seats. Their perma-grins resolute, their platitudes well rehearsed, their guff just keeps on coming -

" We must raise the bar, we need more blue sky sharing between core strategic units and only then can we make the vital business decisions end to end. I have high expectations of you, I want you to have high expectations of me, ladies and gentleman I theng yoo…".

Had we been at a political conference I'm sure the party leader would have delivered the rallying call late rather than early but today, our MD takes the opportunity to rev up his troops before lunch. He tells us he believes in us, we're a great team and it's time now to take the next step into a successful future. Sir Trevor then invites questions to our esteemed leader who receives them in earnest. The microphone is passed around the huge, never ending room and faceless colleagues put forward pre-prepared questions that have been vetted to ensure they don't embarrass. It's still only morning so no chance of addled drinkers grabbing the microphone and posing inappropriate questions having been egged on by equally half cut colleagues. So it's straight forward brown nosing all the way, eg, "Can I ask, what is your vision for the company's growth over the short to medium term?" I swear there was an audible groan when that pearler came out.

Forty five minutes in and we're losing the will to live. Imprisoned at our circular tables, eyes front but glazing over, we sit straight but are slouching inside as we dutifully absorb the business speak. It's all high level talk that means absolutely nothing to the vast majority of the people subjected to it. Take Tom sat next to me. He's driven here from his terraced house in Ward End having dropped off his two kids at school while his wife cracks on with her cleaning job at a local pub. She had to walk to work because her ten year old Vauxhall Astra is in the garage having a new clutch. Tom rang the garage on the way in to make sure they didn't intend to fleece his wife when she went to collect her motor later that day. He likes football, bacon and eggs, internet porn and playing darts down the club. He works at the bank purely to make ends meet, to pay his way in life, he is around twenty levels junior to the Executive speaking on stage and is quite happy to be so. The global vision of the bank and all that goes with it is of no interest to him whatsoever. He feels so far removed from the Executive and their objectives that he may aswell be on another planet. He doesn't belie their importance and their commitment, he simply feels no desire to have them share it with him from a platform. He is not sat there pondering the potential improved efficiencies of European finance, he is sat wondering if the lunchtime buffet will be any good and trying to work out the story line to last night's first part of a two part Taggart.

This is all no-one's fault. It's the world we live in when we sign up to work in a bank or any other hulking great organisation. The Executive have the purest of intentions when organising events like this, they simply wish to remind us all that there are leaders in the business making strategic decisions and it's kind that they consider us, but honestly and truly we don't want to be there to hear it. We accept that the paymasters need to show leadership and we appreciate the sentiment, but we're poles apart. Each of us return to work knowing our attendance, or not, at such an event makes not the slightest jot of difference to how the company will be run henceforth and there's nothing we've been told today that we hadn't already learned from weekly emails from the Communications Department. So while the directors are paraded before us, ushered on and ushered off by a man we're used to seeing on the telly, we sit stupified in a state of complete boredom, entirely neutral to all that's being said. The room is a sea of furrowed brows, pursed lips and grated teeth. Interest feigned, breaths deep, stomachs rumbling. Bored, bored, bored. Only one question remains of our Executive. When is lunch?

Tom's patience is rewarded with a hot plate of beef chilli. Wolfing it down, he rings Tracey to make sure the garage hasn't shafted her and is relieved to find they haven't. I polish off a couple of platefuls before cheesecake tips me over the edge, I return for the afternoon session feeling like I do at about 4pm on a Christmas Day, absolutely stuffed and ready for a sleep. But this is no time for slumber, Sir Trev is off again.

"Welcome back," he says dramatically as if returning after an ad break, we dutifully chortle. "I've come here today because I was offered the chance of an interview," he announces. I'd assumed he was here to pocket a substantial fee for the easiest days work of his life but I was clearly wrong. "Could you therefore give a warm welcome for your Operations Director, Mr Michael Morris."

At this point Michael Morris gets to his feet and shifts his overweight frame and grey, balding 53 year old head across to the left hand side of the stage where Sir Trevor is waiting for him, perched upon the tallest stool I have ever seen. Michael totters onto stage and takes not a little time in negotiating his way onto an identical stool opposite Trev. Once aboard he peers down at the floor and dangles his feet out to see if they reach it, they don't by some distance. He holds on to the sides and awaits the first question. He has nothing to fear other than the long drop, in a somewhat stilted Q&A session he's delivered an over of easy balls that he swats to the boundary without fuss. "Has the bank gained ground on its competitors over the last twelve months?... Do you feel you have the best people in the industry working for you?" That sort of thing. It was amusing watching our Operations Director take this interview in his stride, untroubled, as if a guest on Parky. He was dealing here with one of the country's most renowned interviewers, someone who'd chewed the fat with Thatcher, Mandela, Clinton, you name it, yet he didn't flap and carried on regardless. I doubt Trevor would number this among his all time favourite interviews with answers detailing statistics, projections and proposals but in this respect it was no different than were he talking to a politician. For us, it was no different to listening to a politician, our concentration waning by the second.

Interview over, it was back to presentations, as another director, this time female, took to the stage. If we had felt bamboozled by the torrent of jargon up to this point, we hadn't heard anything yet, the

Communications Director delivering a masterclass in how not to communicate, switching off her audience in five minutes flat. Never had I heard so many sentences constructed with so little day to day English and so much business speak and banking phraseology. It was traumatic to listen to, forty whole minutes of highly faluted guff that I can't bear to repeat. I promise you you'll forgive me. If the morning session had been a toe curler, this was simply the most mind numbing forty minutes of my life. Thank goodness the 'energiser session' was up next…

… the quirky, fun, interactive slot. Today it would be presented by two guys, both ex-bank, proving nepotism ain't dead, who'd been drafted in to talk to us on the subject of perceptions. Perceptions of ourselves and of others, and perceptions others may have of us. Sound anal? It was. Up on screen a powerpoint showed a pie chart with four different coloured quarters. Each colour had within it a list of six personality traits to describe four very different types of person and we were invited to select which of those colours described us best. I was green for the record. Not sure why I tell you this, it's of no importance. Anyway, the session was adequate in that it saved us from further torture by business speak, but the presenters were dealing with an already defeated audience. We laughed limply in certain places, sniggered gently at their double entendres, but forgot both individuals the moment they stepped off stage. Their theories were all very interesting but they disappeared up their own rear ends with an over analytical critique of the human psyche when we'd long since lost interest and started planning the pre-dinner drinks back at the hotel. Ever the cynic, I consigned this perception presentation to the memory dustbin. Be yourself and they'll buy you, try and be someone you're not and they won't.

Finally the conference ended, with Sir Trevor McDonald bidding us a good night, smiling widely as he folded away his papers. He'd done a good job, been a convivial host and dropped in the occasional life saving one liner here and there to stave off rigor mortis in the audience. Delegates drifted away to find their carriages back to the hotel. I made a mental note to book a day's holiday same time next year, I wasn't going to sit through one of these again.

CHAPTER NINE

"...I love this life and all it's shown..."

In the fight for promotion, this game was critical. Eight games of the season remained and today our opposition was the third placed team immediately above us, and remember the top three gained promotion. If we lost, we fell nine points behind them, if we won, we'd close the gap to three points with a much easier run-in than they. We had to win.

Fourteen showed up this week, players not spectators, (we'd kill for an attendance that big). The usual suspects were there and there was the welcome addition of Ian Harley, who'd been persuaded to turn out having wilted under the persuasive pressure of our midfielder and his good friend, Podge, the previous night. I remembered him well. When I was in opposition to him in my St Mary's days, he'd lead us a merry dance with his close ball control and trickery, though he'd clearly seen more of the high life since then, he'd put a fair bit of timber on. Also amongst our number was Ian, sent off in disgrace last time out. I was delighted that he'd pitched up, a Christian league was surely the league above all others prepared to offer forgiveness to players who'd erred, however seriously, as long as they were contrite and showed a willingness to change their ways. When he'd left the pitch a couple of weeks ago I wasn't sure whether we'd see him again, he'd said some pretty unsavoury things to the linesman and I wasn't sure if St Thomas were prepared to have him back, but thankfully he was to be given his opportunity. It'd be one of his last appearances for a while though, a 35 day ban would be been meted out to him by the Birmingham Leagues within a few weeks.

You very often sense a beaten team before it takes to the field, ill-prepared and lacking concentration, shoulders slumped and in no particular hurry to get started, but equally a bunch of relaxed but determined team-mates gives the opposite impression, anything but victory doesn't seem possible and today was that day. Our garish orange shirts were once again dragged on to our pasty, lily white torsos and our departure hastened from the dressing room when Pig lived up to his nickname with a fearful guff, the stench filling the room in an instant. If ever Rob needed a mechanism to raise his sluggish, lacklustre team from their dressing room slumbers and out onto the pitch in time for kick-off, he'd found it in Pig's rear end.

After my so so performance in our previous game, it was a relief to hear I'd been selected at left back. I'd stank the pitch up in the second half last time out and wouldn't have been surprised had the manager 'given me a rest'. But we didn't have many left sided players, so Rob didn't have too many options when selecting a left back and I got the nod. As ever, I offered a prayer before the match began, not with the team but on my own, I hadn't plucked up the courage to pray with them as a group yet. I always ask God to keep everyone on the pitch safe from injury, to give us his Holy Spirit in order that the game may be played in a sporting manner and I ask that everyone finishes the game believing they've acquitted themselves well and have not let anyone down with their performance. If I'm honest I'm thinking mostly of myself with that last request but others also, there's no worse sinking feeling than leaving the pitch having cost your team the game. I'm confident God answers my prayer, though not always in a manner I expect. We've had injuries, we've had heated atmospheres in games, we've had players let themselves down, me included, and it's at this point I might turn to God and ask him what happened to that prayer I'd offered before the game? But God is God, it's not for me to try and understand him or work him out, He works through our lives in a way He sees fit and I'm happy with that. I pray not necessarily for God's benefit, he doesn't really need my instruction, but it reminds me of the dependency I have on Him and that I need to remember to bring all things before Him. I've grown to learn that a wish list placed before God isn't one that He receives and ticks off one by one to my order, He knows best but it does me no harm to remember to keep bringing my desires before Him as a reminder to me that He is the guiding light in my life.

The first eleven read as follows – Rob, Andy, Joe, Chris Preece, me, Chas, Podge, Pig, Buzz, Affers and Mark. Clem was disappointed to be on the bench and I felt for him knowing how dispiriting it can be when you learn you've been sidelined. He was joined by Ian Pearsall and Ian

Harley, before the game all three were promised they'd get on during the match. This can be taken in two ways, it's good to know you'll get a game, it also feels somewhat patronising however, as if you're being patted on the head for making up the numbers and being accommodated with a fifteen minute run out as a thank you. This is seldom the intention but often the perception. I'd been substitute enough times to know what mind games can go on in your head.

Unintentionally, I provided the entertainment in the pre-match kickabout. Crosses were pinged over from both wings into the penalty box to be converted, or sliced wide, by the dozen or so would be centre forwards awaiting. Except that is for me, who stood resolute as the sole defender, repelling every cross I could reach with a header or heaving volley. This caused much hilarity, I don't quite know why, I suppose I was meant to be trying to score too but I reminded my team-mates that defending was a serious business and needed practicing every bit as much as their laboured goal attempts. This sounded all very well until the next cross came over and I sliced it horribly off my left shin and into the net. Not the greatest confidence booster moments before kick-off.

The referee today was Andy Dixon, an occasional member of St Thomas congregation though I doubted our opposition were aware of this. Had they been I'm sure they'd have read nothing into it, the referees in our league are indisputably neutral whatever their background and referee the games as they see it with no bias at all. You could say that they're as bad as each other but you said that not me. Once again we had two official linesmen, I had no idea what we had done to deserve such an honour, and I was concerned to find that one of the linesmen was the guy Ian had severely abused a couple of weeks ago. He must have been surprised seeing Ian in our squad so soon after his indiscretion and I felt an explanation was in order but didn't get the opportunity as the game kicked off moments after I'd spotted him.

Pardon me while my head swells to twice it's normal size, but this was the best game of football I'd played since playing up front for Boldmere Middle School 25 years ago. I had one of those games to outweigh the horror shows I'd provided in seasons past, a near faultless display of tackling, heading and even passing. My every involvement seemed to come out the way I'd intended and I was fair chuffed. If the ball fell to me in open play, I managed to find a team-mate with my pass, if the ball drifted in the air towards my receding temples, I headed it firmly and if there was a 50/50 tackle to be won, I won it. It was a great feeling to hear those around me so congratulatory as I made a telling interception, their encouragement spurred me on, though I figured it was more out of shock than admiration. And to cap my best first half in years, the referee overlooked a blatant handball by my good self on the halfway line momentarily before I cleared the ball forward with a tremendous hoof for it to land at the feet of our centre forward Mark who was instantly brought down in the box for a penalty. He strode up to slot the penalty in himself, I claimed an assist for setting it up. Life surely couldn't be better than this, playing a blinder and being an integral part in your team's one nil lead in a match critical to your promotion chase. I was loving it. The half-time whistle went and I felt like waving to the crowd as I left the arena to take a well earned break. Was Steve McLaren watching? England were having trouble with the left back position since Ashley Cole had gone off the boil, maybe I'd played myself into contention.

I revelled in the half time black slapping. Nobody had played badly, all of us merited our congratulation, but since the stand out moments of the half had centred on yours truly in the final five minutes, it was I that happily received all the plaudits. I feigned modesty as best I could, appearing to be in earnest concentration as team-mates shook me by the hand, but really I was thrilled to bits. Yes it was the most minor of minor leagues and yes, the game would be forgotten by all and sundry within half an hour of the final whistle, but right now I felt like Bobby Moore. I thanked God for giving me this feeling of elation remembering to bolt on a plea at the end that he could see his way to guiding me through the second half without undoing all the hard work.

He was faithful to me in the second half and I saw out the game relatively uninvolved but untroubled. It was Mark Hadden's turn to shine as he followed his first half penalty with three goals in two minutes, a scruffy tap in, a close range header and a Rooney-esque lob over the keeper from 25 yards. Rob subbed him after an hour with the game effectively won at 4-0, a move manager's normally make in the professional game to engineer a standing ovation for the scoring hero as he leaves the pitch. The sentiment was certainly there from Rob, but it didn't have quite the same effect with Mark accepting the applause of two subs and the manager's wife, Sheila. Not to worry, the thought was there. We panicked a little when Zion pulled two goals back in quick succession with ten minutes remaining, and it prompted the tired old cliches from Messrs Preece and Rodgers "We've switched off lads haven't we eh?... come on St T's, to the finish, to the finish..." but Zion had left themselves too much to do and the game ended 4-2 in our favour. We'd closed the gap to three points on our nearest promotion contenders.

Reaching the touchline after the final whistle, we congratulated one another on a job well done then drifted off to take the nets and goalposts down. Well not all of us, there's always a few who suddenly develop cramp or sit on the ground nursing supposed knocks while the rest of us do the donkey work. It's somewhat chastening having to drag down the nets after being soundly beaten, almost like the final insult, your penitence for defeat, but it can be a joyous occasion when you've won as you gather together like a gaggle of excitable schoolkids, swapping stories of the match, wildly embellishing your involvement. We carted the goalposts off to the padlocked yard for another week and here's a tip to all you amateur footballers who find yourselves having to do the same. Make for the goalposts nearest their destination if you can remember to have the presence of mind so to do, otherwise you'll be left, like me, with only two others for company as you haul your set of posts an extra hundred odd yards after ninety minutes of football. Either that or feign cramp like the rest.

CHAPTER TEN

"... no matter what you do, it all returns to you..."

Bit of a relief when I opened my post the following Monday. Hot on the heels of my three points for speeding into Birmingham recently, 39mph in an unpopulated three lane carriageway earning me this and a sixty quid fine, I had it confirmed that my 91 in a 70 on my way back from Scotland just before Christmas, would earn me only three points.

What an idiot I'd been to allow myself to gather nine penalty points on my licence. Did I ever learn? Five years ago I'd reached twelve points, only avoiding a ban when accepting a place on a Speed Awareness course. Had I learned nothing on that day?

I worked for a timber company as a sales rep at the time, they provided me with a Golf GTI which I liked to stretch towards the limits of its potential, you don't buy a stereo and play it low being my theory. But having boasted a clean licence for ten years, I clattered up nine penalty points in the blink of an eye, all for speeding, and as a result found myself just one more offence from a driving ban.

I'd been a travelling salesman for years and years, averaging thirty thousand miles a year. At one time it was more like sixty thousand, when my sales territory wasn't '*Midlands*' but '*the UK*'. I'd once driven from my Birmingham home to a morning meeting in Rochdale (two hours), headed south in the afternoon for a Bournemouth appointment (a further six hours) before rounding off the day dining with clients in London, (after another three hours behind the wheel). When clocking up those sorts of miles, I was destined to register the odd point on my licence for camera recorded indiscretions, and I duly obliged. Sitting on nine points becalmed my driving, I drove like a monk (assuming monks drove sedately) yet after a while the speed began to creep back up and I became more blasé about the possible existence of a camera behind every corner, until finally a lapse, when driving at thirty six mph through a thirty mph zone. A grey speed camera with luminous striping winked to confirm its acknowledgement of my speed.

I received notification of this in the post. The letter explained the likely outcome of my offence was three penalty points and a £60 fine. The fine was irritating, the three points however were potentially crippling, taking me as they did to the twelve point mark and meriting a ban, albeit a brief one, but long enough to jeopardise my job. What good was I as a travelling salesman when I couldn't travel? Panicking, I rang the DVLA in Swansea.

"Yes, I wonder if you can help me. I have nine points and have just received notification that I'm getting another three. Can you confirm if I need to reach twelve or exceed twelve points to get a ban."

"Reach twelve," came the curt reply from a straight talking, South Walian female. "Give me your licence number and I'll check your details on our system."

I obliged and meekly awaited confirmation.

"Oh yes, you'll be banned," she barked, sounding quite chipper about the whole affair. "Your offences have all come within a three year period, that's a ban," she sang triumphantly before saying "OK?" in an inquisitive voice, as if giving me an opportunity to insist that actually, no it wasn't ok, and could I kindly have three points knocked off to redress matters.

Crestfallen, I replaced the receiver and contemplated my dilemma. Would my employers act on my behalf in court and plead that no ban be given to this valued member of staff upon whom the very existence of the company relied? If I were banned, would BSW hold my job open while I served my time? Would they provide a desk job for the length of the ban or might they boot me unceremoniously from employment, for sullying the company's name? They'd been pretty unpredictable up till now as an employer, there was no telling how they'd react. I just had to hope that they'd co-operate and continue to pay the monthly wage which covered the mortgage and other sundries, which all of a sudden were hanging over my head like a rain cloud.

A telephone conversation with a colleague didn't set my mind at rest. Nigel had been in this very situation twelve months prior and explained that it was only because he was having a good spell in terms of sales figures, that BSW had supported him. He'd got the distinct impression that had he been struggling, they'd have happily relinquished his services. Damn. I was experiencing no such good fortune with my sales figures lately, I'd shifted less timber in the last three months than at any time in my two years with the firm, and though my boss wasn't applying pressure, he'd begun to register enough disappointment to have me squirming uncomfortably in my seat. Things did not appear favourable, and I soon found myself leafing through the recruitment pages of the Evening Mail, searching for jobs that did not require a driving licence, just in case the axe fell at BSW. But then, out of the blue, a lifesaver. A letter through the post, again from Staffordshire Police...

"Staffordshire Police are offering you the opportunity to attend a one day speed awareness course in lieu of the 3 penalty points recently issued to you for your speeding offence. You have the choice of accepting the 3 penalty points or taking part on the course at a cost of £95 whereby your penalty points will become invalid..."

This was terrific. For the sake of £95 and a day off work, I could cling on to the driving licence upon which my livelihood depended. I couldn't send the acceptance form back quick enough, never had I been more eager to part with ninety five quid.

The day of the Speed Awareness course came. It was early May, bright, sunny and warm. The course was to be held within the grounds of a nature reserve in Staffordshire, I set off in plenty of time, the twenty mile drive turning into something of a master class in careful, measured driving as I sallied along at pedestrian pace, attempting to encourage within myself a mindset of composure which might hold me in good stead once I arrived at the course. I'd become a little fraught in advance of the day and wanted to becalm myself before arriving. Added to this, the last thing I needed was to get a speeding ticket while on the way to a Speed Awareness course, I'd never live it down.

Having left home with plenty of time to spare, I arrived bang on 9.00am, having taken a wrong turn along the way. For ten panicked minutes the legally paced driving had gone out the window as I careered back on track, screeching my car to a halt in a puff of smoke on the gravel laid car park before sprinting to the Staffs Nature Reserve corporate suite for registration with today's hosts, Travelright Road

Safety Unit. I wasn't sure what to expect once I was there, a row of policemen with arms folded looking down their noses at another common criminal or an officious headmistress type, booking delegates in without looking up from her desk. More likely, a caretaker scratching his head saying, "You've come to the wrong place son, we ramble and look for rare birds here." Instead, I found a tidy and spacious reception area with chairs and tables laid out and gravitated towards the gaggle of people filling in forms handed out by a middle aged chap wearing a suit and tie.

"I'm here for the Speed Awareness course," I gasped.

"Welcome, and thank you for being so punctual. Could I have your driving licence please?" replied the seated fellow with a smile and a straightened back. I wasn't expecting such a warm response, it was rather relaxing. I handed my licence over. The recipient sucked air between his teeth, as if a builder quoting for an extension.

"We have been rather a naughty boy haven't we? Still, you're in the right place to do something about it. Getcherself a coffee and fill this form in, the rest of our crew today are waiting in the room at the bottom. We start in five minutes." He seemed a bit odd.

The room was generous in size. At one end, a row of privacy screens separated the delegates from the sellofane wrapped buffet lunch lying in wait, and at the other, the ominous sight of an overhead projector, laptop computer and blank wall promising the audience a slow death by powerpoint. Tables and chairs were arranged in a horseshoe for the fifteen attendees and up front stood three presenters.

First of the three to speak was an enormous, balding Asian fellow with a Giant Haystacks physique, and a ponytail reaching down to brush the belt that strapped his huge trousers to his hips.

"Good morning everyone, I'm Derek, and first of all may I say CALM DOWN! You all look so nervous, I assure you there's nothing to be frightened of. Just by being here you've made a big step forward and should be proud of yourselves". (This was sounding more like an Alcoholics Anonymous meeting than a speeding course).

"House rules first and foremost. If there's a fire, the fire exits are at the rear of the room ...but you'll have to beat me to get there first heh,

heh, heh," (a well rehearsed line). "The toilets are through the door that you came in, girls to the left, boys to the right. Feel free to leave the room at any time if you hear the call of nature." Very clever I thought, given the course was being run at a nature reserve. I looked around the room to exchange knowing smiles with someone else who may have been tickled by this clever reference, but was met with blank faces.

Very soon, presenter Derek was going around the horseshoe inviting people to a) describe what kind of car we drove and b) provide the approximate number of miles we drove in a year. There was no need for introductions, everyone had been asked to write their name on a card and place it in front of them. Anyone walking in the room could have been forgiven for thinking they'd stumbled over a TV game show rehearsal.

Ann was first to reply.

"I have a little Peugot, I only drive to the school and back to drop off the kids in the morning. I shouldn't be here by rights, they've put a new camera in round the corner from me and I just didn't see it. It's not on really, one day it wasn't there and the next it was and I was running late cos Kylie had forgotten her school bag and we'd had to go back for it, I mean, it's comin' to somethin' when you get done for getting' yer kids to school on time in the morning. There's blokes zoomin' along at sixty some nights outside our 'ouse and I was only doin' 38 at a time of day when…"

"Yes, thank you Ann," Derek interjected, "If I can ask everyone to be brief and simply answer the question. Alan, how about you, what car do you drive and how many miles a year?"

"Well I must live on the same street as Ann because I was done doing no more than a sensible speed for the time of day, but because the police these days have nothing better to do than make money out of perfectly good drivers unfortunate enough to exceed speed limits that are set way too low for the roads they're on…"

"Again, I'd ask you to be brief Alan, what car do you drive?" a concerned looking Derek asked, trying to reign in his excitable audience.

"Rover, ten thousand a year," said Alan, put out by the abrupt end to his opening salvo, leaning back in his seat, arms folded.

Next up was Richard. The Burberry baseball cap and dangling gold chain gave some indication of what was to be expected, and he didn't disappoint, puffing out his chest as he announced to the room his ownership of a Ford XR3i 2 litre turbo. You could just picture it; a white love magnet (his perspective only) with red Go Faster stripe, gigantic spoiler, alloy wheels and windows wound down to enable the world to benefit from his thumping bass.

Derek dutifully toured the row of delegates sat before him, losing the will to live by the time he reached me, perched at the end who told him sharply and with not a little sarcasm, "Golf, thirty thousand miles."

Having thanked the fifteen of us for our contributions, despite the protracted nature of them, Derek gleefully switched on his projector to reveal the first slide of the day – the agenda. It read -

Staffordshire Speed Awareness Course
Timetable: Morning Theory Session

- Excuses for speeding
- What 'causes' you to speed
- Circumstances
- Consequences
- What can you do?
- 'Scenario' Workshops
- Conclusion and 'final thought'

Refreshment break 11.00am to 11.15am
Buffet luch 12.00 noon to 12.30pm
Afternoon On-road Practical session: 12.30pm to 4.30pm

- Practical session objectives explained
- Meet your instructor
- On-road training
- Instructor debrief and feedback
- Course conclusion

Derek continued his presentation after outlining the timetable for the day while his two co-presenters, yet to introduce themselves, sat stoically alongside, grinning at his lame asides and nodding sagely when serious subject matter warranted.

"Hands up those in this room who are here because they were caught speeding?" As expected, fifteen hands poked the air.

"And who was caught exceeding a 30 mph limit but not going faster than 40?". Again, fifteen limbs reached for the sky. He had us in the palm of his hand.

"Well I'm here to help you work out just what the consequences of that action could have been," he insisted in a seamless link to slide two, brought up with a nonchalant nod to his co-presenter, eagerly operating the slideshow. This was the first time presenter two had been called upon and he marvelled in the moment, reaching forward to theatrically nudge a key on the laptop before sitting back with a smug smile and laboured folding of arms.

Derek waffled on but his audience's attention was shifting away from his face and down to his armpits. Being a huge bloke carrying twenty stone or more, the warm atmosphere of the room was causing him to sweat profusely and large, dark, circles had formed on his brown shirt at the top of his sleeves. They made for pretty unsightly viewing. Oblivious, he flourished his arms as he pointed to the slide show, providing a bird's eye view of the damage done to his shirt's armpits. As the damp patches grew, eyes turned to windows, wall posters, feet, anywhere that would spare the sight of Derek's sweaty oxsters and, perhaps realising that he was losing his audience's attention though knowing not why, he moved the agenda on to a group discussion, mercifully lowering his arms by his sides as he did so, the sigh of relief in the room almost audible.

" What causes people to speed?" he asked.

The question was met with silence, an air of disinterest beginning to set in already. This lasted for several seconds before co-presenter Trevor stepped forward, the silence too much for him. Trevor was around fifty, a bank manager type with a very deliberate delivery. He wore a grey suit, white shirt with spotted yellow tie and was the only person in the room declaring a plastic visitors badge upon his person. He was spindly, turn him sideways and you'd struggle to see him.

"Well Derek, I have to tell you," he opened, "and I hope this doesn't shock you too much, I used to speed and do you know what? Sometimes... I still do!". He theatrically placed his right index finger to his lips while propping up the elbow of his right arm with his left hand. He'd delivered this statement as if he were announcing to his wife that he was leaving her for another woman. He continued, "But I have learned to control my driving so that if I do find myself over the speed limit for the particular road I find myself driving upon, whether that be a country road, a road in a built up area or whatever, my offence will be merely marginal and I soon drop back comfortably within the legal limit. And do you know why?" (pause for dramatic effect), "because I learned Derek, yes, I learned, that I didn't need to speed, I engaged in a brand new mental fix whereby I refused to live life in a hurry." And with that, Trevor stared at his subjects, swung himself around to face his chair, sat down, and threw up his head to gaze serenely out of the window, his nose pointing towards the ceiling. He seemed to be waiting for a standing ovation. He didn't receive it, instead he got the silent treatment afforded to Derek moments earlier. I looked around for evidence of tumbleweed. These silences were getting painful.

Out of pity, to spare Derek's pride, I punctured the silence.

"I speed to get there quicker," I said, before closing my eyes in instant acceptance of the stupidity of this contribution. As the room laughed at my statement of the bleeding obvious, I flushed with embarrassment. I wasn't trying to be clever, it just came out wrong, but I did have a serious point if they'd just be patient.

"What I mean by that is life is so hectic, with pressures on us to cram so much into every day, that I find myself rushing around, driving faster than I ought." My supplementary appeared to redeem me somewhat, but served also to bring Trevor back into the conversation.

"Absolutely Alex and I'd like to thank you very much indeed for that contribution. This is precisely my point. Why speed? Why get there earlier? What is the hurry? Once you realise there is no need to rush around like a man possessed, or of course a woman, you find yourself driving at a sensible speed. Simple. No more tickets for speeding, no more accidents."

Tracey couldn't contain herself, "You obviously ay got three kids ave ya mate," she piped up with anger. "I ave to get three of em ready, out the door, in the car and at school for arf eight, then be at work ten miles away for nine o'clock. You try it." She wailed in quite a temper. For someone who looked like she'd not been listening all morning, she'd made quite an entrance.

Trevor was unmoved however and explained to Tracey that simply by emerging from her pit earlier than normal, and organising breakfast and the dressing of her kids more efficiently, she could leave the house with sufficient time to spare. His breathtaking simplification of a process that every parent can sympathise with, the morning helter skelter, drew intakes of breath from the audience and had Tracey coming back for more. The men winced and looked forlornly at Trevor in anticipation of Tracey's riposte. Incensed by his naivety, she tore into him while giving us all the benefit of her life history which incorporated a divorce, a separation, and confirmation that her three kids were fathered by three different men (one of whom was locked up). Perhaps, she suggested, Trevor could give her some pointers as to how she should organise her time more efficiently when faced with three young children first thing in the morning, who had no father figure around. Chastened by this, Trevor refused the opportunity to reply, and like the leader of the opposition left dumbfounded by an answer from the Prime Minister at Question Time, didn't bother with a follow up. Instead, he looked desperately around the room for a new contributor. He didn't have to wait long. Now Tracey had piped up, the floodgates were open, and the next twenty minutes degenerated into a free for all with people explaining why it was unjust that they were here today, the police should be out looking for real criminals.

Several individual cases were outlined with few contributors accepting guilt for their 'offence'. The excuses for their speeding beyond the legal limit ranged from being pregnant to being late for a football match, driving an unfamiliar new car to not realising that the local speed camera had a film in it. Only when sixty year old Terry went off on one in disgust at an MP being let off for clocking up over a hundred mph, simply because a stomach complaint meant he needed the toilet in a hurry, did Trevor reign the conversation back in, retaking the moral high ground.

" We should ensure time management becomes, if you will, modus operendi," announced Trevor, delighted with his unscripted break into Latin. Looks were exchanged between myself and the others, what was modus operandi? I assumed it meant 'standard practice' but wasn't going to embarrass myself by asking. Trevor left matters there, rejoicing in his Latin induced glory, and took his seat before Tracey could dive in for round two.

Derek moved forward to present the next item on the agenda, scratching his burgeoning stomach, his shirt stretched across his midriff, the buttons at the point of bursting. It seemed churlish to suggest he needed a breakfast what with him being so large but the audible rumbling emanating from his gut, suggested he'd not eaten that morning. Conscious that everyone could hear his stomach, he apologised and explained he wasn't feeling quite right today following a meal the previous night. He patted his belly once or twice and pressed on but then, having nodded to Trevor to bring up the next slide on the overhead projector, he turned to face the screen with his back to the audience, and inexplicably broke wind. It wasn't a faint sound but a clear drone akin to Sid James blowing a raspberry in a Carry On film. If you could hear a pin drop when Derek had thrown out the first question of the day, you could hear a feather drop now. The boy racer's body convulsed as he held in his laughter, rocking to and fro, a grin spreading wide across his face. Others were grinning too, desperately withholding their mirth, it was always a guaranteed comedy moment, a non deliberate guff in public. Ann wasn't smiling. She was horrified and looked daggers into Derek's eyes, appalled at his anal announcement, and the old guy, Terry, wasn't impressed either. "I haven't come here to be farted at," he barked.

Derek turned around to face the victims of his indiscretion and said nothing, deciding not to make an issue of the matter. He opted for this way out rather than apologise and potentially increase his already acute embarrassment. There was no denying he'd broken wind but better to leave the unmentionable unmentioned than make a fullsome acknowledgment and embarrass oneself further appeared to be his thinking, and this was understandable. To say his behaviour had the audience distracted would be an understatement, the boy racer deeming the occasion worthy of a text message to his mates. Pleased with his morning's work despite the obvious setback, Derek invited everyone to the buffet bar that lay behind the screens. He wasn't to join us, still feeling the effects of last night's Chinese, and left for some fresh air instead. It was doubtful he'd tell his partner that evening about his embarrassing wind episode, it was definite that we'd all tell ours.

Lunch saw the fifteen delegates file around a table boasting the barest of essentials in its claim to be a buffet lunch. No frills, no extras, simply sandwiches with three different fillings, crisps, sausage rolls, cheese flan and orange juice. We shuffled in line around the table, populating our paper plates with tired looking fare, before standing by the wall, munching away, endeavouring to avoid conversation. A couple of chats were started but soon ended, I didn't get the feeling that lasting friendships would be borne of today. Many reverted to the sanctuary of their mobile phones, the customary safety net should face to face conversation prove too much. It reminded me of the Chris Eubank incident when, hounded by the attention of paparazzi, he pretended to be speaking on his mobile phone, only for it to ring.

The afternoon session was introduced by Trevor. He had surely been a tax collector or fire safety officer in a former life. He looked like a robot, talked like a robot and gave the sense that his whole presentation was memorised so seamless was the delivery. He opened up with an 'energiser', intending to raise his audience from their post lunch slumber.

"Could everyone stand up please," he said, "and reach as high into the air as you possibly can, that's right, stand on your tiptoes and reach with your fingers as high as you can." Trevor joined in by reaching skyward, unfortunately revealing that armpit hell was something of a stock in trade with Travelright Road Safety, though it wasn't as spectacular as Derek's.

"Now," he continued, barely able to speak having reached his full height in an effort to reach the ceiling, "try and reach that little bit further... OK..., now rest."

Delighted with himself, Trevor beamed, "Did you see what you did? What every single one of you did? Yes, you all reached that little bit further despite me having asked you the first time to reach as high as you possibly could. This just shows you that no matter how hard you strive, you can always improve by trying just that little bit harder. Now be seated." He was well chuffed with himself and glowed with pride as his two co-presenters shook their heads at each other, rolling their eyes, no doubt having witnessed this performance several times before. I resented being a stooge in someone else's act.

"Now that bit of fun is over, let's take a little look at what we learned this morning shall we?" he suggested. "Who'd like to tell me just one point that they have learned from this morning's session?"

This was going to be fun, whenever a teacher put out a question like this back at school, he'd be greeted with a wall of silence and sure enough, nobody in the group replied. It was left to Trevor to address individuals directly in an attempt to shame them into a reply, and he picked on me first, but before I could answer, Alan dived in to unleash the pent up indignation he'd harboured since an answer of his had been cut short in the morning.

"I've learned that if I don't want to pay through the nose for my insurance, I shouldn't get tickets for driving four miles an hour over the speed limit in bloody Cannock. They should set these cameras to trigger at least eight miles an hour over I reckon, not bloody four. My insurance has gone sky high cos of this speedin' ticket and I'm not happy about payin' ninety odd quid for today neither."

Trevor wasn't sure what to say in response to Alan's outburst, so said nothing. Instead, he moved straight along to slide one of his show which showed a photograph of a busy road, filled with obstacles such as zebra crossings, pedestrians wishing to cross, traffic lights and road signs. This was to be the first of three scenarios which we were asked to regard for five minutes. A pencil and paper were laid out for us to compile a list detailing potential dangers, Trevor also asked us to note down the legal speed limit in each scenario. I was labouring under the effects of half a dozen sausage rolls and a quiche, and decided to leave the list compilation to others while pouring myself some water.

"OK, who thinks the speed limit here is forty? "Six hands went up and about the same number of nods in the affirmative, before Trevor loudly interjected, "No. It's thirty. We've learnt very little from this morning haven't we?"

This particular classroom was beginning to feel a trifle alienated by their school teacher. It was tempting to ping chewed up lumps of paper at him with our rulers, or leave upturned drawing pins on his seat, but we needed to co-operate in order that we complete this course and avoid the dreaded three penalty points. Trevor knew this, it empowered him, he knew his criticisms would go relatively unchallenged and he appeared to wallow in the safely held self importance he could exude. He knew his stuff, he knew the audience didn't, and he knew everyone in the room would just have to sit back and listen to him bellyache if their licences were to remain intact. The power trip was clearly as much a joy to Trevor as it was an irritation to me, but I could do nothing about it.

The robotic, monotone delivery continued from Trevor, this barely alive cardboard cut out of a human being, his feeble asides and hints at humour doing nothing to ease the pain of a stupified audience. The presentation was littered with the kind of nothing phrases that had us cringing, "Done that and got the t-shirt, you don't know what you've got till it's gone, if I had a pound every time I heard someone say that... .etc, etc, etc." The slow, deliberate voice and motionless nature of the presenter didn't help. Only when describing the difference between a 'speed' limit and a 'safe' limit did Trevor become anything approaching animated, "Country lanes may carry a 60mph legal speed limit but could this limit be realistically condoned when your car approaches a tight bend, say, near the entrance to a farm? You'd be observing a speed limit but certainly not a safe one," he opined.

I had had quite enough by now, I was bored, so began to construct a picture in my mind of what I perceived Trevor's life to entail beyond these four walls. Listening to this guy for what seemed like hours now,

I reckoned I had a pretty good handle on what he was all about. Fifty two, two teenage girls ready for university, a semi detached house with lawn front and back bordered by colourful flower beds tended by a dutiful wife with nothing better to do in between coffee mornings, tupperware parties and making hubby's dinner. No doubt he drove a Rover saloon, kept it immaculately clean and secured his seat belt even if he were only reversing the car out of his garage. He was probably a member of a golf club, if not it would be bridge or tennis, he could conceivably be a Mason but maybe found that a little intimidating so became a member of the school council instead. His wife would do the laundry, the cooking, the ironing, he would do the breadwinning, the lawns and the driving and they'd both live happily ever after, their daughters marrying accountants or bank managers.

Only when I'd moved on to the horrific image of Trevor being involved in carnal cavorting with his wife was I interrupted.

"Did you hear the question Alex?"

"Sorry, could you repeat it?"

"Certainly. What potential hazards can you see on the screen?"

"Erm, that pub looks a bit close for comfort, might have to pop in there for a swift half if the traffic was heavy and getting me down." Some laughed, others were too disinterested to register a reaction.

"I was thinking more in terms of the sweet shop on the left hand side. We've seen the obvious dangers but I'd like you all to start looking at the less obvious now. Remember? Reach that little bit higher? Small children may be rushing out of that sweety shop flushed with the joy of having bought a bag of liqourice allsorts and be oblivious to the road in front of them, what may happen then?"

I pondered a while. Should I come up with a facetious line to raise a laugh, bring some life to proceedings and burst Colonel Blimp's bubble, or was it best to count to ten and give the obvious answer Trevor was looking for so they could all get this turgid afternoon over with.

"They could step in front of an oncoming car Trevor," I said in a low voice, "but I have to say, I'm pretty cautious by nature and I'd like to think I would be aware of kids at the side of the road."

"Cautious by nature are we Alex? Then why, pray, are you here today? Hmm? I'll tell you, because you have been far from cautious and may I venture, perhaps a little reckless, in speeding beyond the legal limit." The atmosphere heightened as the room awaited my comeback, but there was not to be one. I decided silence rather than interaction was going to get everybody out of this room sooner rather than later, so kept my mouth firmly shut. Triumphant at having had the last word, Trevor moved on.

The fractious nature of the proceedings continued as the agenda was ploughed through, until the classroom work mercifully ceased, and it was out onto the open road for a drive with an instructor. Three to a car, one instructor and two students, with each taking it in turns to drive a few miles on different types of road so as to learn what dangers to look out for and what speeds to drive at. The afternoon proved much more exciting than the morning, not least when I was asked to slow down having approached a speed camera in a 40mph zone while hacking along at 60mph, almost becoming the first delegate on a speed awareness course to be clocked speeding at fifty per cent over the legal limit. In the event, my drive proved adequate for a pass mark from the instructor and by four o'clock I was back in the classroom for a fond farewell by the indomitable Trevor. We were all told we'd successfully passed the course and were free to drive home carefully. He hoped never to see our faces again. The feeling was mutual.

This latest indiscretion on the roads, returning from Scotland, was going to cost me dear if it were repeated. One more speeding ticket and I'd hit the twelve point mark and this time they wouldn't be so lenient as to offer me a place on a speed awareness course. It'd be a straight ban and no mistake. What was I thinking of belting down the M74 that day before Christmas? I remembered precisely the moment I was caught by the camera. It was under a motorway bridge near Moffat, as I turned Radio 4 off because somebody about my age on Desert Island Discs, I forget who, had kept me waiting ages before choosing her next track. I was holding out for The Smiths or something of that ilk, she'd chosen flippin' Tchaikovsky's finale to Swan Lake or something and I remember looking up as I switched the radio off and seeing a mobile camera unit flash ominously from an overhead bridge.

It was my own stupid fault, although I held modern technology partly to blame. Not the speed camera, but in car trinkets like I-Pods, sat navs and mobiles. I'd lost focus on the road with all these gizzmos sitting around me, sometimes I'd have the mobile phone ringing on the hands free while I was unplugging the sat nav from the cigarette lighter and swapping it for the I-Pod transmitter, it was like sitting in Jim'll-Fix-It's armchair all these bits and bobs surrounding me. I rather think it should be illegal having all these toys working simultaneously as you drive, you could add DVD players in the back if you wanted, and the last thing on your mind can be driving sometimes when you're waffling on to a mate on the handsfree while the sat nav woman's telling you to go left and right. Oh for the days when I'd bowl along in my Mini Clubman, my only concern being could I get from A to B without conking out. I don't remember ever reaching nine points in that and if I'd plugged in a sat nav it'd have been worth more than the car.

CHAPTER ELEVEN

"... everything I want's within my grasp, it's time to nail my colours to the mast..."

My wife thinks I'm turning into a nerd. This isn't a complete shock, I spend too much time in front of the computer, still, it's a bit of a wounder when your spouse reckons you should be wearing an orange cagoule and trainspotting on a Saturday afternoon.

I like the internet. Well, message boards mostly, forums where otherwise timid people become as brave as lions, keyboard warriors giving the world the benefit of their wisdom without fear of redress or accountability. I'm great at it. Sitting there in my own front room, pontificating about all and sundry. You can reinvent yourself if you like. Nobody off the message board has met you, so if you're a shy, reserved fellow who gets tongue tied if someone asks you the time, you can suddenly become a colossus in your own lunchtime, delivering your opinions in measured tone, who's to know you've taken an hour and a half to come up with that killer line? You get your idiots on there, wind up merchants and crowd baiters who start up threads intending to outrage, you just don't rise to it, but reading the replies from people who do can be entertaining. I tend to concentrate on the same forums, you get to know people better that way, what makes them tick and what they like to discuss, I'm usually on Heroes & Villains (a Villa supporter's website). I'll use the internet to further my education one day, in the meantime I'll carry on discussing why Paul Weller is overrated and how irritating it is when people drive close to your bumper. Kate's right, I'm a fully signed up nerd of the modern age but I'm quite enjoying it. And I can order my anorak online.

I read somewhere that professional footballers prepare for a match with a long sleep, a plate of carbohydrates, then a massage. My preparation for today's mid morning kick-off was a 6.15am alarm call from Emily, a sausage sandwich with brown sauce and two hours of ironing.

I don't half get the trots on a matchday morning. Before leaving the house I spend more time on the throne than the Queen. "Better out than in," as my father used to say when leaving the bathroom and telling us to, "Leave it ten minutes if I were you," and if you saw the quality of the toilets in our league you're best getting things out of your system before leaving your front door. I wonder what it is about your body that tells it to be apprehensive to the point where you must empty yourself before a game? For years I've been playing football but every Saturday it's the same. Jonny Wilkinson was playing his first England international in three years later today and was reported to have confessed to the pre-match squits, so if it was good enough for him to insult the porcelain for twenty minutes before a match then it was good enough for me. Still, you don't want to hear about my bowel movements, let's move on.

We were playing Selly Oak today and I knew absolutely nothing about them, they'd joined the league just last season, when I played in a separate division. I sneaked a look at their page on the league website to see if there were any handy looking lads to look out for but to my relief, found instead a collection of youngsters, yet to fill out, who I expected to brush off the ball without fuss. They'd struggled this season, losing eight of their eleven games and with us on a roll I felt confident we could turn this lot over.

It was the familiar scene for a cold winter's day at our home ground as we assembled pitch side an hour before kick-off. Our squad were poking and prodding the frost ridden pitch, nervous that the game may be called off by an over cautious referee. All of us were in animated agreement that the game should be on, the referee was harangued with the usual comments as his perplexed expression intensfied, 'It takes a stud... the sun'll burn it off... it's not frosty in the goalmouth.' We wanted the game on, no-one wants to leave their pit early on a Saturday morning to find it's all been in vain. The ref said he'd be keeping us in suspenders for half an hour or so, reserving judgement to give the piercing sunlight a chance to see off the white top. Thankfully the welcoming sight of green emerged from beneath during that time, so we fetched the nets, it was game on.

Pig had brought his stereo player to boom out nightmare dance trance, or whatever you call it, in the changing rooms before the game. Motivational he called it, insufferable more like, so when he was first to pop outside for a warm up, I took the chance to put on The Wedding Present CD I'd brought along. It lasted one and a half songs, my indie thrash as disagreeable to the majority of the team as Pig's one dimensional din was to me. Matt Brady dragged it off in favour of more non-descript bilge of the modern day youth. Not to worry, I'd heard at least one full song, and could run out with the anthemic 'Everyone Thinks He Looks Daft' ringing in my ears. Rich Taylor described The Wedding Present's music as 'dirge' as we got changed which I took offence to, dirge to me meant music of sluggish morbidity, Radiohead kind of stuff, but he comforted me when explaining 'dirge' had more credibility than that and when he compared it favourably to The Smiths and Bob Dylan I was happy.

Our warm up was far more organised this week now that Matt Brady was back, more organised in that it actually took place. When he's not around each player just does their own thing which never amounts to much, shots in at the keeper or a natter on the halfway line with the ref. But today we were giving it the full jog across the pitch, kicking up our heels one way and knees up the other, we looked all professional. When we turned to complete our fifth width of the pitch I was ready to fly the white flag so knackered was I, how was I going to last ninety minutes if I felt exhausted completing a low tempo warm up? I put my hands on my knees and took a deep breath, I hoped the opposition's strikers weren't fast or I'd be dead in the water.

We were superb in the first half as the bright sunlight warmed the air, turning the morning from Winter to Spring. Our orange shirted team battering the yellow shirted opposition, it was like Holland against Watford. Hold on, that would make me Neeskins at the back and Matt Challoner as Cruyff up front, something wrong there, but you get the point. Our superiority was stark, a welcome relief to an ageing centre back like me since it ensured I had little to do except patrol the halfway line and repel any aerial balls that came my way, of which there were few. However, there are no points dished out for high percentages of possession and territorial advantage, goals are what count and we contrived to miss a hatful of chances, including a penalty, to go in scoreless at half time. You had to feel for Mark as he stepped up to take his penalty kick. Around thirty under fourteen year olds stood gawping behind the goal as they arrived for their game kicking off an hour later on an adjacent pitch, and the pressure of this sudden audience seemed to put him off. I don't think St Thomas has ever played before a crowd so big. It must have got to him, his penalty failing to test the keeper and instead testing the strength of the branches in the tree behind the goal as they intercepted the ball on it's journey to the car park.

The second half found midfielder Podge constantly telling me to 'tuck in' as we awaited Selly Oak's goal kicks. I've been told to ' tuck in' hundreds of time before but have never yet had the courage to ask what on earth this means, (in the same way I've never had the guts to order beef bourguignon in a restaurant because I can't pronounce it without sounding stupid). In the heat of battle there's no time for protracted conversation on the subject of footballing terminology otherwise I'd ask him what 'tucking in' involves, and how you're supposed to 'express yourself' when playing football, so I'll just keep nodding until his back's turned then take up my usual position. And it was from this position that I saw Affers play his last part in the game. He challenged for a ball as it came down from the skies and took an elbow in the face for his trouble, a lump the size of a ping pong ball immediately forming above his left eye as he lay prone on the floor. By the time he left the pitch three minutes later he looked like a freak, a ledge of swollen flesh hooding his eye as he peered from beneath to find his way off. On came Ian Pearsall as his replacement, his final appearance before the thirty five day ban he'd earned for his sending off at Amblecote.

The resultant free kick provided the game's most incompetent passage of play, with me at the heart, kicking off the sorry chain of events. I'd had another good game, sweeping away anything that came my way by head or by wallop, and could only point to one occasion where a striker had got the better of me. I can defend, I'm confident of that, but give me a dead ball to kick and my achilles heel is found. So why I volunteered to take this free kick from the halfway line I don't know. Well I didn't volunteer, our entire team scarpered into the opposition box waiting for someone to launch the ball into it and I was the last man standing. It was about forty yards I needed to kick it, no problem with a moving ball that I could volley, but a nightmare if the ball's stationary. I took a gulp, a stuttering run up and heaved my right foot at the ball, the result wasn't good, my effort grubbing along the ground apologetically, my team mates standing hands on hips as they watched from the opposing penalty box. A startled opposition striker stood ten yards in front of me, was taken aback as the ball arrived at his feet and so surprised was he that he allowed it to bounce off his shinpad and back towards me, it was a chance to make amends and this time with a moving ball. I took another swipe but sliced the ball horribly, the result as wide as it was long, the ball reaching Buzz as he retreated from their penalty box. He aimed a lofted pass into the area but over cooked it so much that it drifted out of play without bouncing. I daren't look to see if the under fourteens were still watching, Rob Hill was watching though, he dropped his head and shook it in despair.

This was a turning point. With half an hour to go and us as dominant as we had been in the first half, the passage of inept play that had just unfolded appeared to galvanise the team and there were plenty of encouraging screams from orange shirts, "Come on lads... switch the head on boys... we're better than this," the usual fare. From then on we converted our possession into goals with Mark scoring two, Matt Brady one and the Reverend Rich Taylor notching as well, an accurate side footer into the net from twelve yards after one of his parishioners had laid across a square ball. In between our goalscoring spree, Pig took the trouble to break a window belonging to an old people's residential home that stands beyond a high wall alongside the pitch. It was a cracking interception as he volleyed the ball fiercely from the feet of an onrushing Selly Oak midfielder but after the ball scaled the wall, we heard the shatter of glass. Personally I think it's disgraceful that one of our players should reduce himself to such wanton vandalism on the old and frail of our community, and I told Pig so during a break in play. He rightly pointed out that when I find myself in that home in just a few years time, he promised to visit me by means of redress. The story of Pig and the broken window doesn't end there. Ten minutes later he was substituted and decided to return to the dressing rooms to grab a jacket. While back in the clubhouse, a commotion was going on with a fifty odd year old woman lying on the floor outside in great distress. Pig, being a sports injury physio, felt he could use a little of his experience to help the patient as she writhed on the deck, so he rolled up his sleeves and got stuck in while someone called an ambulance. It turned out the woman had broken her ankle, and who was this woman? The friend of the manageress of the old people's home that Pig had destructed with his hoofed clearance, that's who. Having learned of the incident, she'd marched straight out to have a word with the Manager of the Stick & Wicket and on her ascent of the steps at the entrance, had taken a tumble and now found herself being nursed by the architect of her distress. Priceless. Pig didn't let on and sensibly so. This was like something out of a Terry & June set.

We were comfortable 4-0 winners in the end, closing out the match without alarm. There's normally a flurry in your own goalmouth towards the death of any game, regardless of the quality of the opposition, defenders back off, fatigue meaning they play too deep as their tired limbs render them unable to keep up with play. I keep saying 'them' but I suppose I mean 'me' really. Daz had come on as sub at left back with fifteen minutes to go and kept imploring me to move up and catch them offside but I reminded him that I was 37 years of age, cream crackered, and had no intention of making myself look foolish by chasing a guy half my age back to my goal because we'd mucked up an offside trap.

Rob Hill has a knack, just like a previous manager of mine Alan Pidgeon, of taking the wind right out of your sails within seconds of the final whistle. When you've put your all in and leave the pitch having secured a clean sheet and put four past the opposition, a touch of ego stroking and exhuberant congratulation wouldn't go amiss, but we reached the sidelines today for Rob to announce, "We've got Walsall next week, need to win that or the promotion push stops there." This may have been true but wasn't necessarily the battle cry the troops wanted to hear at this juncture. We refrained from relieving Rob of his crutches and clouting him around the head with them, but only just.

Instead it was off to the dressing room for a spot of childish joshing and bravado filled talk of promotion. I stripped off and headed for the showers, it's open plan showering at our place, four showers opposite another four. A couple of other players joined me and we showered while discussing the game, being careful not to catch a glimpse of each other's furniture. It's something of a taboo and very much left unsaid, but I'd venture that very few men feel overly comfortable standing stark naked in a shower next to another man revealing his glory, or otherwise, but we get on with it with puffed out chests and deeper voices pretending that there's nothing unusual or uncomfortable about it all. It's perhaps something us blokes carry from childhood, where we're required to shower or get changed with other kids at school.

We'd done ourselves no harm today with this comfortable victory and later learned that the team above us had only drawn against lowly opposition. Promotion was very much within our grasp now, we just needed to keep winning. Six games left, the top three to go up, the league table looked like this –

	Played	Points
City Church	12	26
Rowley College	9	25
Zion Athletic	13	23
Us	12	22
Dynamo Kingswinford	10	19
Halesowen Zion	10	18
Selly Oak Methodist	12	7
Brierley Hill AOG	9	5
St Boniface	10	5
Walsall Olympic	11	1

CHAPTER TWELVE

"... there is more to learn than I aim for..."

Harry and Hattie are my children from my first marriage. Every Wednesday I collect them after school, from their home in Tamworth, and they stay overnight before I return them in the morning. I see them every Saturday too, one weekend for the afternoon, the following overnight. This is the 'access' agreed, horrible word 'access' but the best description I can give for the time I'm allocated.

They are terrific kids. Every father says that, I'd question a Dad who didn't, but I don't get a moment's bother with them, or is that absent father syndrome? Does their mother see behaviour that I don't, since she's with them far more than I am? I suspect this is the case. Like it or not, their visits to me are just that, 'visits', and seem to be viewed by them almost as a day out, an adventure away from the daily grind of predictable home life. It's not a situation I'm entirely comfortable with, I don't want to be considered a celebrity in their life, but conversely I can't deny it's a thrill being perceived as a fun Dad. Whether I'd be considered as such were they to live with me full time I don't know, but I get the feeling that they look towards our time together as something a little out of the ordinary, removed from the norm of day to day life, and maybe that's not such a bad thing. They have a loving mother, a three year old sister through their Mum's second marriage, a sound stepfather and a settled family life with a local school providing good education and many friends. They've been through a lot but they also have a lot.

When Harry was about to turn three years of age, and Hattie was four months away from being born, I left the family home. I didn't leave my children, I left my marriage for the good of all parties, it wasn't an easy decision. It's too painful to revisit in any great detail, as distressing a time in life as you could imagine, not least for my then wife and our son Harry who was left bewildered when his father was no longer around having been there for him every day for three years. There were no third parties involved, neither Michelle nor myself were planning a life with another, I took the decision that we needed to part after eleven years together and it was a very trying time. We had a messy couple of years after that, understandably so, access rights and financial arrangements all needed to be agreed, but this is behind us. To cover years of separation, upheaval and upset in a few words seems callous, maybe flippant, suffice to say it's a familiar episode in many people's lives these days and the trauma cannot be underestimated for those going through it, not least the children. What I would point out to those who suggest parents should stay together for the sake of the children, and it's understandable that people leap to that conclusion, is that in many cases parents should part for the sake of their children. If differences are such that they cannot be worked out and are irretrievably damaged, bringing up children in an environment of discord and disharmony, to put it politely, is not what is best for them. I'll end it there.

Despite it being an away fixture, we tried to get our game against Walsall Olympic switched to our ground. Their pitch, the fabled Anchor Muddow, was an utter quagmire whereas ours was comfortably the best pitch in the division, relatively flat and grassy all through the winter, and with their ground being less than a mile away from ours, it surely wasn't going to put them out to play at The Stick & Wicket instead. Any talk of home advantage in our league is laughable. It's not as if anyone has a home terrace of thousands behind one goal, sucking the ball into the net with the vehemence of their vocal backing. And we're not playing golf here, there are no greens to read, giving a regular player an advantage in terms of which way the ball's likely to roll. The only home advantage anyone could claim in our league is knowing where not to take a dump before the game in case you catch something. In the event however, the deep blanket of snow that the UK woke up to on the Thursday put paid to our chances of football on either pitch, the match was called off.

This country excels in blind panic when the weather takes a turn for the worse, it's headline news when a tree blows over in Norfolk or a school's closed in Gateshead because the pipes have frozen, but on this occasion the country was genuinely blighted by severe snow. It prevented Harry and Hattie staying over with me on the Wednesday for fear of me being unable to drive them the 16 miles back for school the following day. I used to love the winter when I went to school as a teenager in Scotland. Our school was in the east coast town of Stonehaven and kids from all of the surrounding villages took the bus in each morning. Downfalls of snow, of which there were many, left the roads treacherous and had the Rector cancelling school at the drop of a hat to prevent accidents from panicked bus drivers, sliding around the narrow country lanes as they drove hundreds of kids into Stoney. There was no point opening the school just for the kids from the town so it would be shut full stop, leaving us to stay at home in the warm. We loved it.

The midweek snow in Aldridge didn't alter my working day, I was due to stay at home anyway. The beauty of working from home as I do, a 'Location Independent Worker' to give it it's official title, is that time is your own, you manage your diary as you see fit. So if you've spent a few consecutive days driving up and down the motorways of the Midlands visiting customers and feeling as if you've had no time to breathe in between, a day spent at home is just what the doctor ordered. An opportunity to rise when you want to, four month old children permitting, pad around in your scruffs, and complete your paperwork or emails in your own good time. And when the World Cup's on in the summer, well, diary planning becomes something of an art form. The Sky TV Guide is not a magazine I normally open when it arrives unrequested on my doorstep, but when there's a major sporting event being shown during the week, perhaps at strange hours if it's being hosted in a foreign country, I hoover up the start times and manage my working diary accordingly. Sounds good doesn't it, but it's easy to abuse if you don't have self discipline. It's when you leave an afternoon blank in your diary because Murder She Wrote or Columbo's on that you want to worry, and there are people out there who simply couldn't work at home because they wouldn't trust themselves to be disciplined enough. I can't deny the occasional afternoon on the golf course or at the shops when the mood takes, but as long as your boss is happy with your overall output, or sales figures in my case, there's no grounds for concern.

I had a written application to prepare for a customer I'd recently seen, it was going to take a couple of hours and I was still in two minds whether to proceed. I didn't trust them. It's my job to visit companies, listen to their funding requirements, then apply on their behalf to our Credit Department if I believe they are trustworthy and have a genuine need for the money. (Bear with me, bank speak isn't rivetting but stay with it). An early tip I was given by my first boss at the bank was, "If it was your money you were lending to them, and not the bank's, would you lend it?" In the case of this particular customer I wasn't sure.

They imported soft drinks in large quantities and sold them on to smaller wholesalers in smaller quantities. They made their money by marking up the sales price to ensure there was a tidy profit. But there was something about this particular organisaton that didn't ring true, something niffed, it reminded me of a similar operation that I'd signed up a few years back that subsequently defrauded us by thirty odd grand. You get a nose for suspicious customers after a while, and become cautious when everything appears too good to be true. Another line comes to mind, "If it seems too good to be true, it's normally because it is." The fraudulent customer I'd signed up a while back certainly fell into the 'too good to be true' category. The business made ready made meals and supplied them to pubs, clubs and restuarants, it was a very new business, just a few months old, and had received its first order for £35,000. Their customer was delaying payment and so we advanced money to our punter on the strength of the £35,000 due to be paid to him. The owner was a huge man of Asian origin, a long heavy beard and dull brown eyes. He wore light brown Indian dress from head to foot, baggy linen trousers with a silky buttonless top adorned by a silk scarf wrapped several times around his neck. He was a very pleasant guy, too pleasant perhaps, because my every question was accommodated by the perfect answer. He seemed one step ahead, knowing the sorts of questions I'd be asking and which type scripted answers to provide. We operate a kind of 'tick box' system at the bank, various criteria need to be met, and unsurprisingly looking back, he ticked all of them, and with a disconcerting smile as if he knew something I didn't. All requests for information were met promptly, all searches carried out on his business and on him as an individual proved squeaky clean, there was no technical reason on earth to reject this man's application for funding. He had an apparently professional operation, a succession of staff coming in and out while I was at his premises and in every respect it appeared to be a pukka outfit. So we gave the money... and he stiffed us. Never saw hide nor hare of him again, nor our thirty odd grand.

And here I was again. Different person, same scenario. Everything in the garden looking rosy but I sensed the thorns weren't far from the surface. I 'had all the drains up' to coin a phrase, I investigated this company and the individuals long and hard but found nothing but glowing references and recommendations. Again, this was a new business and again, this seemed the perfect prospective client for the bank to provide it's money to, but I was filled with deja vu. The premises were well stocked, the operation seemed slick, the company seemed genuine. The owner smiled knowingly and spoke with coy enthusiasm as he delivered expert answers to questions he knew were very pertinent, all boxes ticked. I had no reason to doubt him other than a sixth sense about him as an individual, and my painful experience of the meal man a couple of years prior. My nose twitched with the scent of something unpleasant, my knees knocked a little as he put pen to paper, but I went ahead and signed him up the next week. I couldn't find an earthly reason to turn him down and risked a complaint from the customer were I to turn him away with no good reason, and the prospect of no future introductions from his bank manager. I held my nose, signed him up, and kept him on the books for...

...oooh, all of five minutes. The guy stung us for ten grand and scarpered never to be seen again. That's twice I've been strung up like a kipper by fraudsters now and it aint gonna happen again, not if I want to stay in a job anyway. Feel sorry for us? Didn't think so, representing the bank when annual profits outstrip the gross national product of a small country doesn't tend to engineer sympathy from the wider general public.

CHAPTER THIRTEEN

"...all my life I've felt so uptight, now it's all alright..."

Some time in the early nineties I was sat on a train pulling out of Crewe station, returning home to Birmingham after a meeting up north. I was working in the timber trade at that time and since the company's flagship sawmill was in Carlisle, I often found myself up there for sales meetings, and that day it had been a particularly gruelling one, our boss taking us to the cleaners for not having sold enough timber in recent months. Battered and bruised, I was making for home with a flea in my ear.

It was a hot Summer's day, not the day to be sat on a stuffy, overcrowded train for three hours or more. As the engine grumbled into action and took us slowly away, an intimidating shaved headen guy, rucksack strapped to his back and eyes wild as oats, marched up and down the carriage, randomly stopping to talk to people. Well not so much talk to them as berate and harangue them, until their disinterest was such that he moved on to the next unsuspecting victim. He was around thirty years of age and out to make his point.

"Are you born again?" he demanded of a quivering Granny sat minding her own business, her handbag clasped to her chest. She didn't answer, she just looked frightened.

"And how about you?" he shouted, turning to a young student sat oblivious, eyes closed as he jerked his head to his Walkman.

Rising to his full height, the rucksacked weirdo raised his chin and delivered a semi-sermon for the benefit of anyone who cared to listen. He had a captive audience, we weren't going anywhere unless we felt like chucking ourselves off the train onto a Staffordshire embankment, which was becoming a temptation, so he continued unchallenged.

"Today you are blind but one day your eyes will be opened when He comes to judge us. And what will he say? What will our Lord say to you who have scorned Him? Depart from me, I never knew you." he bellowed, totally unabashed at the spectacle he was making of himself. The deafening silence from his audience leaving him with only the sound of the train's wheels clattering over the tracks as a response, but this did not discourage him. "No-one comes to the Father except through me. I am the Way, the Truth and the Life..." he continued. This was quite a claim I thought, that I might only find God through a thuggish looking character with torn jeans and a haversack.

He moved on a little further up the carriage and addressed a spectacled, businessman who peered over his newspaper to tell him to "F*** off" and I had to agree. These bloody born again Christians, who did they think they were? Bouncing around the earth like a bunch of brain washed moonies, telling us all that they had something in their lives that we hadn't and it was about time we shaped up. It was them that needed to f***ing well shape up. Yeah, shape up and ship out, they needed sticking on an island where they could beat their collective breasts as one, a brainwashed community swapping stories of their God, Father, Son, Jesus... whoever it happened to be that day, while we got on with real life. Bunch of idiots.

Around that time I was editing a football fanzine and had published a poem on the back cover which was a spoof of the Lord's prayer. I substituted as many words as I could for names of current and former Villa players. I thought nothing of it but received plenty of criticism from Christian readers for my 'crass insult'. Hadn't these people got a lighter side? What with miserable readers and nutty born again passengers joining at Crewe, Christians had swiftly promoted themselves high onto my list of distasteful figures. I had always held them in low esteem, now it was getting lower. I found them to be weak, wimpish, irritating, self satisfied and above all, a bunch of do gooders who assumed I wanted to be done good to when I bloody well didn't. I was more than happy in my selfish, self absorbed world thank you very much where I was out for me and no-one else. It was every man for himself in this world and the sooner they got around to my way of thinking the better. They could butt out and God bother someone else. Not for a minute did I believe they had the interests of anyone at heart but themselves, they did good deeds because they were conscripted to do so, I did good deeds because I felt like it not because I'd been told to. They could stick their God, Jesus, Moses or whoever where the sun seldom shone.

Wind on fifteen years and I now find myself attending a church house group on a weekly basis, St Thomas every Sunday morning and describing myself first and foremost as a Christian. Funny how things change isn't it? I'm not a street preaching nutjob, not a smug self satisfied know it all (much) and not all the things I assumed Christians to be. It appears I was wrong all along and am happy to admit it, there was something in this Christian malarkey after all, it just took me years of rebellion and cynicism before I found what life's actually for, or more accurately, who it's for.

How did this happen? Well, because I hit the bottom. I'd bought a large bottle of aspirin, placed it in a carrier bag with a bottle of water and made for the woods. Life to me simply was not worth living anymore. My children were offered to me for an hour here, a couple of hours there, my depression was such that I'd been banged up in a mental ward for ten days for my own safety, my alcoholism had reached epic proportions where if I wasn't asleep I was drunk, drinking or hungover. It was a tragic time and had lasted for a sustained enough period to reduce me to ribbons. I'd had it. Then God found me. Sounds twee doesn't it? Seems weird, unbelievable. But He did, or more accurately, I found Him, He'd been there all along I just hadn't looked. With my earthly tent looking thin, my face drawn and pale, and the colour in my eyes long since turned to grey, I looked washed up. Then a man called Phil Hall met me for lunch at a hotel in Stoke for a business meeting, it was the Autumn of 2000. Within ten minutes of us sitting down together he called a halt to business talk to tell me I looked awful. He asked me to describe where I was at in life, what had happened to reduce me to this pale shadow of a person, weak in speech, the lights flickering behind my eyes but no-one home. I told him the full nine yards; about my messy divorce, separation from my children and the trauma it brought, how drink had been an issue for years and had me in a vice like grip, and how my depression had taken root to an extent that there didn't seem a way out, to the point that I was past caring. He told me there was an answer, something that would pull me out of the depths and set me back on a road to peace and happiness. "Have you asked God into your life?" he suggested.

I was furious. I trusted Phil, enough to talk candidly about my private life, because he seemed genuinely compassionate and eager to help, yet here came the truth, he was another of these bleedin' Christians ready to meddle in my affairs and try and impose his mythical God upon me. I told him what he could do with his God. But he didn't take offence, he listened patiently before speaking again.

"Tell me, you've arrived at this point in your life under your own steam having not involved God at any time or attempted any type of relationship with Him. What can you lose by investigating the issue? What if I'm right and you're wrong? You could be missing out on a renewed, transformed life. Alex, God will not let you down. Read a part of this book tonight and call me tomorrow". He offered me a book, I forget the name of it but it contained testimonies of twelve sporting people whose names I was familiar with (Langer, Edwards, Akabusi, Tiga Mala). They spoke of where their lives had been taken and how God had become real to them. I did read part of it that night while holed up in my bedsit, it was inspiring but I was still dismissive, believing all of these sportsman to have misplaced their loyalty and trust. They'd got where they'd got with their own efforts, no-one else's, and if they believed otherwise then more fool them. But I read on. At the back of the book a short prayer was given and the reader asked to commit it to God. I remember sitting there on my bed in the sparsely furnished, tiny combined bedroom and living area of my bedsit, looking at the wall and feeling as low as I ever had. That it should come to this, sat alone in such pathetic living quarters, depressed, under-weight, looking like a ghost and with no future except the next drink. And just when I thought it couldn't get worse, here I was about to utter my first prayer to a God I didn't believe in. Christ this was bad.

This was the prayer —

Lord,

You know me. You know me better than I know myself. You know I've turned away from you and lived my life apart from you. I turn to you now to ask your forgiveness, to ask you to come into my life, to be real to me, to forgive my sins and to renew my mind, body and soul. I give my worries, woes and despair to you. Come into my life Lord and set me on a path of peace. I pray this in your holy name Jesus

Amen

There were tears as I finished it. Not harrowing gulps of distress laden howling like you see on TV dramas, but a couple of drops down my cheek as I sat slumped on my bed with my back against the wall, tired, shrivelled and most of all, beaten. I felt as if my last breath had been breathed, I felt completely exhausted, I remember a sense of actually feeling dead already. I had nothing more to give, no energy to take another step, this was my bottom. I fell asleep to be woken an hour later by the telephone.

" Hi Al". It was my Granny. She very rarely telephoned, once in a blue moon. We had a chat, my Granny telling me how much she loved me and supported me, it was nice. I put the phone down to her and after a few seconds my Mum rang, we held a similar conversation. Later, after I'd read a little more of the book, Stu rang, ever concerned, and we made plans to meet the following day. I didn't tell any of them about my meeting with Phil that day, the book or the prayer, I felt too embarrassed, but already I was feeling a little better, almost alive. Three phone calls in quick succession from people I loved, this to me wasn't a coincidence but a message. Perhaps there was something in this after all, perhaps and only perhaps. For now I was going to give God the benefit of the doubt but I wasn't convinced by any means. However, a little part of my cyncism and hard heartedness had been broken this night and as day passed day thereafter, God very gradually became more real in my life and as I handed my life to Him and His will, it was transformed.

What does 'handing your life to God or to Jesus mean?' Sounds a bit weird doesn't it. Well to me it is simply an acknowledgement that there is more to your life than just you, there is a spiritual dimension, and you involve God in it. God's our father, you can function without Him, as I did, and take what you get from your own efforts, or you can function with Him and have a life more purposeful and peaceful. I explain it to my children this way – I'm your Daddy on earth and if you need something, you come to me to ask for it. I can't help you unless you speak to me about your needs, tell me what it is you need, involve me. By the same token, how can God help you in your life if you haven't communicated with Him, asked Him, talked to Him? He's there for you but if you don't knock on his door how can he answer it? When you do speak to Him you might not always get what you want. He knows what's good for your life and what isn't good, but you must keep going to Him and realise the importance He has in your life. You may ask God for things that aren't granted but don't be despondent, live by His will and that's all you truly need, just as a father on earth knows five bars of chocolate one after another isn't good for his children however much they want it, God your Father knows what's good for you and what isn't.

My beef with God used to be that it was cruel for Him to wait for me to reach such a catastrophic low point, after years of unhappiness, before he stooped to help me off my knees. But I look on it like this now; it was me that shunned him. He was there all along, I just didn't open the door to Him …I'm drifting down cliche alley now and no-one likes a bible basher so let's just say then that if you need help but never ask for it how can anyone ever help you? And the argument I always held that Christians always get you when you're down is more real to me now then ever, I'm glad they do or I don't know where I'd be today.

So here I was tonight at Bev's ministry training group, 'Mission Possible'. I entered the course in typical fashion, with a thirst for knowledge, ready to ask questions and demand answers. I don't attend these groups to nod and agree in the right places, I go with a healthy cynicism to challenge the biblical truth put before me. Some may squirm in their seats while I probe and question the words of the bible but I see it as my duty to ask questions of my faith and not accept spoon-fed words that I struggle to interpret. When I'm in the community, in day to day life, spending time with far more non-Christians than believers, I may appear devout, resolute, firm in the face of any ridicule, but put me in a room of Christians and I let all my doubts hang out, my measure of unbelief there for all to see. It's then that I'm reminded of my human frailty, my shortcomings, my unrealistic desire to be all knowing. Spiritual warfare some refer to it as, but in my heart of hearts I know who will truly come out on top and that's what faith is isn't it? If you demand proof it's no longer faith. God gave us free will, he didn't issue Christian straight jackets to a world of robots, we're asked to seek Him. If I try to understand fully, intellectually grasp all that is implied, suggested and told by the bible, I'm on a loser. It's a collection of sixty six books comprising nearly 800,000 words. Believe it, accept it, live with it has become my motto. Try and understand it all and you'll be a gibbering wreck by tea-time.

Rob Hill and I had taken part in Bev Mann's six weekly course at the church since the turn of the year. Bev was training for lay ministry (being a voluntary, unpaid priest effectively) and was required to run a course on the subject of evangelism for half a dozen people or so as part of her qualification, we'd agreed to take part before we realised it was on the same night as football training, Tuesdays. Not to worry, the nights had grown very cold into February and it was no hardship telling the rest of the lads that we couldn't make their outdoor six-a-side in the freezing cold, we'd be drinking hot coffee and eating garibaldis instead. Of the nine participants, Rob and I could certainly be called the most cynical and challenging, we gave Bev a hard time week after week, throwing open the same questions that Christians and atheists have alike. Why would God allow suffering? Why is there so much pain in the world? She had a torrid time from us.

Thousands of people become Christians every week, but why? What happens in their lives that suddenly, or more likely gradually, they feel God is real to them for the first time? Not everyone has a 'Paul on the road to Damascus' type conversion, very few people can point to a moment in time, an overnight experience, where God all of a sudden became known to them, it's exciting to hear testimonies from people who do have such an encounter, but in the majority of cases it's a gradual acceptance of God rather than an instant conversion.

Jan Coleman was a member of Bev's group and I had the opportunity to discover where her Christian life began. She was 35 before she even considered the subject of God, it hadn't entered her head until then. Brought up within a loveless family as a younger sister, an accident at birth, she never felt accepted by her father and didn't have much of a relationship with her mother either. She'd tiptoe around the family home, shunned by her family, terrified of life, until fleeing the nest at 17. Relationships with people thereafter were a trial, never trusting anyone, always expecting rejection, she was a timid, withdrawn and frightened young woman, directionless, despairing and down.

One evening somebody from St Thomas church knocked on her front door and told her about a course called Down Your Street, a six weekly course explaining the basics of the Christian faith to those who might be interested, and held in the setting of their own home. Jan said okay and miraculously her husband did too, despite being a confirmed atheist. She had expected him to turn the invitation down flat but God's spirit seemed already to be flowing. As the course began, Jan felt very much an outsider and couldn't really connect with what was being said, others appeared to be embracing the course while she felt like she was floundering, but by week two she found God was beginning to speak to her through the material they were reading and the people she was meeting. Excitement grew within her and instead of sitting on the periphery of the group, and day to day life in general at that time, she began to feel included, wanted. She explained that it was like gradually unwrapping the world's most precious present to find the answer to all of her wants and needs in the middle.

When the six week course finished, she made a commitment to God that she would put Him at the centre of her life, her husband Andrew didn't (but several years later, he did) and since then, her life has changed beyond measure. Previously, she felt nobody had any interest in her, she was inconsequential, the world was going on around her and she wasn't included. Now, she was feeling accepted, loved, wanted. She'd been waiting for this moment all of her life and now it was here, she felt as if someone had put a funnel into her and was sucking out all of the pain, anguish and hurt gathered up over all those years. She was being rid of all the rubbish in her life and in her mind. The old person died, the new person was born, all of the anxieties, concerns and inadequacies had gone and a new beginning was found. There have been wobbles since, crises of faith where the human mind struggles to comprehend the workings of God, but she's never felt God hasn't been there with His guiding hands. And this is just one tale of how God has changed the life of somebody who previously felt lost, inadequate and was despairing. There are countless other stories, mine included, of how God has picked somebody up by their bootstraps and turned their life around, He can do this in anyone, all they need do is ask.

CHAPTER FOURTEEN

"... I was a stone I didn't show emotion..."

Lessons in life number one; never meet your heroes.

I entered a competition run by the Walsall Advertiser; send an email to the Advertiser's offices and you were automatically entered into a draw for tickets to see The Charlatans that forthcoming Sunday evening. Now, my brother Stuart and I have been devout fans of this band since the second of their nine albums, they've been around for years. We've seen them perform over a dozen times and they never disappoint, some bands do, this mob don't. So when a reporter from the Advertiser called me the next day to say I'd been succesful in winning two tickets for the gig at the Birmingham Academy I was ecstatic, but when he explained further that I needed to arrive early to meet the band I couldn't keep my hat on. Meet the band? Hold on a minute, meet The Charlatans? Like, in person! My knees turned to jelly.

I was a bit apprehensive, this could go horribly wrong. I remembered a friend meeting an ex-Villa hero of his to find himself sadly disappointed when said player turned out to be a bit of an arse, what if lead singer Tim Burgess was a pillock too? I'd take the risk, when the chance to meet your heroes is rolled out on a red carpet how can you say no? If you were a James Bond fanatic and had the opportunity to meet Sean Connery, what would you do? Or if in a golfing pro/am your name was drawn alongside Darren Clarke, would you feign illness and stay away? No, I was frightened to death by the prospect of meeting my musical heroes, but I didn't hesitate in accepting the tickets on mine and Stu's behalf.

I rang Stu to give him the good news. Typically, his phone diverted to answer machine, my message leaving him in no uncertain terms that his reply was required urgently. The sternness in my voicemail may have been disconcerting, he called back assuming I was about to announce a family bereavement, but when he heard what I had to tell him, it was he that fell gravely quiet. Eventually he spoke, resisting the onset of hyperventilation.

"Meet them?" he shrieked. "What... like... meet them meet them?"

"Yes, meet them meet them. We're gonna meet The Charlatans!" I squealed like a beehive haired schoolgirl suffering a dose of Beatlemania.

"But I can't," Stu said.

"Eh?"

"I've a meeting in Brighton on Monday morning. I've gotta travel down Sunday afternoon, the train and hotel are both booked," he whined.

As his older brother I felt it my duty to put him straight. He was not going to enjoy the pleasure of this opportunity ever again and it might be prudent, I suggested, for him to re-book the train or travel down on Monday, whatever it took. He asked me to give him thirty minutes to make alternative arrangements, he called back in ten, he was coming.

The Charlatans aren't everyone's cup of tea, but they are ours, with the jammie dodgers to go with it. Indie music has always been our bag and on the indie scene this band have a place secured in the hall of fame, their anthemic hit singles renowned for boosting any festival's lull into a high. Three members of the five piece group are locals, Walsall and Cannock, and I'd actually come across one of them before, when playing golf at Hill Top Golf Club in West Bromwich. The drummer, Jon Brookes, was there playing with his father and I approached him in the cafeteria before we played. It was a brief but pleasant conversation, me thanking him for his music, him thanking me for thanking him for his music, and that was that. Stuart was there too and asked him for his autograph with the never believed suggestion that it was 'for a friend'. In actual fact it was. This particular meeting wasn't terror inducing because it came out of the blue, I paid for my sausage sandwich, turned around and there he was. I hadn't received a phone call forty eight hours prior to invite me to meet him over his fry up in a golf clubhouse, it just happened. Sunday on the other hand was so far in advance that Stuart and I had hours and hours in which to panic.

We were having kittens on the afternoon of the gig, the magnitude of the event just too great for us to take in. What do you say to people who you've never met before, but who's work has been such an intrinsic part of your life? They don't know you but you feel you know them, a little, having played their albums to death and seen them perform so many times. Their interviews in magazines are familiar to you, providing an insight into their personal lives, the lyrics in the songs give further evidence of their personalities and beliefs, and their behaviour on stage has you assuming certain aspects of their personality traits. Then suddenly, there they are, three feet in front of you, and with them waiting for you to say something. You stand in awe, tongue tied, petrified, but pretending not to be. You so desperately want this interaction, as brief as it is, to be perfect. You've dreamt of this moment; the throw away line that makes them laugh uproariously, their reply showing utter admiration of you as they hang in anticipation of your next word. And then after much chortling and guffawing, the lead singer puts his arms around your shoulder, intimates that you're the elusive, blood brother he's been searching for for all of his life, and you walk arm in arm into the sunset before swapping mobile numbers to signal the commencement of a wonderful friendship.

Sitting there nursing soft drinks in the Square Peg that Sunday afternoon, an hour or so before the meet, we attempted to calm each other's nerves without success. The Square Peg's one of those vast Wetherspoon affairs, no music but very loud, as yards and yards of drinkers enjoy cheap ale and hearty conversation. Ours wasn't a conversation, more an exchange of unanswered gabblings, the pair of us nervous wrecks, full of apprehension and fear, talking ten to the dozen, not answering one another, merely throwing out words, as if filling the silence with talk would somehow relax us. I don't know what Stu was worried about, he'd seen this all before. When visiting a pub with a friend in London one Saturday lunchtime, who was at the bar but James Dean Bradfield reading a newspaper, alone with his pint. Having plucked up the courage, Stu had approached him and simply thanked him for the music, wished him a good day and returned to his seat. Bradfield had even sought Stu out to say goodbye as he left the pub. The perfect coming together of musician and fan, no frills, just a two way appreciation of one another and a polite parting of the ways, just how it should be. Somehow today felt different though. Too much anticipation, it wasn't off the cuff, we had too much time to think. So after an hour's wittering, with both of us trying to persuade the other that we were cool with all of this and that we were taking it all in our stride, but failing miserably, we got up to leave.

"I'm just gonna say hello and leave it there," ended Stu, "No point trying to come up with a killer line or get smart quoting their lyrics back to them."

I agreed. "Too right, we'll sound a right pair of charlies if we start telling them how their lyrics have touched our lives or something cheesy like that. They've heard it all before with these meet and greets Stu, there's nothing they won't have heard, let's just say hello and clear off."

We weren't altogether sure what we were going to be walking into. I pictured a room crammed with guests, families, free loaders and road crew, with Stu and me sat on the edges, not actually meeting the band but spotting them across the crowded room. Stu thought differently, he reckoned there'd be ample opportunity to speak with them as we'd be in a room with a handful of other competition winners. Neither of us expected lead singer Tim Burgess to show up, it'd be the drummer and one of the guitarists. This wasn't a problem, we'd be chuffed with that and perhaps a little relieved that we didn't have to face the embarrasment of being tongue tied in front of the lead singer. Agreeing that we should just enjoy the pre-show interlude for what it was, a quick hello and an autograph, but both hoping for so much more, we continued our journey to the venue, the stroll down Dale End feeling like the walk of death.

Next to the Academy venue is Bar Academy, and we'd agreed to meet the Advertiser's reporter there, George Makin. He greeted us as we entered, we'd never met before but our bewildered, star struck faces had given the game away. He reached inside his jacket pocket, produced two tickets for the gig, then asked us to have a drink while we waited for the band's management to call us up to the venue in ten minutes time. Bar Academy is a small, dark pub, dull walls and duller lighting, staff wearing black and most of the punters too. My flushed face provided some well needed lighting as the enormity of the moment began to take hold of me, I had never been this nervous before. Stu and I sipped our cokes and twitched every time the bar room door opened until we got the call after about twenty minutes. All the talk had been done, now we were at the business end of proceedings. Another competition winner walked up with us, looking sickeningly relaxed and chilled. We were delivered to a smiley, happy, blonde female of around twenty five years, and she threw a backstage pass necklace over our heads and led us through some double doors into a room, about half the size of a penalty box. There were deep brown sofas either side, a bar giving free beer and water ahead, and a coffee table adorned with freebies (signed posters, signed CD singles) for us and the other guest. Like two naughty schoolboys, Stuart and I sat down ramrod straight, our faces now as white as a sheet. The last half hour had been like being led to the gallows; the slow march from the Square Peg, the long wait at Bar Academy, the smirking assassin greeting us at the door before leading us to our fate in the depths of the Carling Academy. Stuart accepted the offer of a beer and I nodded a 'yes' to water, I couldn't get my words out.

And then it happened. Within seconds of our arrival, the door opened and in drifted Tim Burgess, Martin Blunt (bassist) and Tony Rogers (keyboardist). "Oh my God," said Stu, "Flippin' eck, Tim Burgess," muttered I, and like two soldiers called to attention, the pair of us rose to our feet as one, and wiped our sweaty palms on our trousers. I don't mind telling you I corpsed spectacularly. Despite the fact that we were given sixty seconds or so to gather ourselves as the infuriatingly calm competition winner we'd walked up with shook hands with the band members, I had nothing of worth to say when Martin Blunt approached me. This despite the fact that he congratulated me on my attire.

" Nice jacket" he said leaning forward to check out the label on the breast pocket "Paul Smith eh?"

I'm not a label junky by any means but had deigned tonight's event worthy of my best. I wore my navy, short length denim jacket with the tiny green Paul Smith label on the front. I thought it offset the boot fit, blue jeans that draped over my blue adidas trainers perfectly. I looked kind of indie but with a bit of class. Stu had deliberately worn his black Harrington jacket knowing it was occasionally favoured by Tim

Burgess, "You can tell it's genuine Harrington Al from the red tartan lining inside." We'd both dressed up by dressing down if you like, except our jackets had been very carefully chosen. We wouldn't normally wear decent gear to a gig, it just gets trashed with smoky smells and beer splashes.

"Thanks," I offered meekly by way of reply, "Just a little somethin' I..." I didn't bother continuing, he'd already moved on to Stu. I turned to observe Stu's conversation with The Charlatans bassist to find him far more lucid than I had been. I forget what they talked about, I wasn't really listening to tell the truth, too busy trying to catch my breath. Stu was smiling and so was Martin so I gathered it was going well. I saw Tony Rogers (the keyboardist) over Stu's shoulder and since he was stood alone, arms folded and looking pretty bored, I ambled over to meet him. He was very friendly, and appeared to make a definite attempt at putting me at my ease, sensing my acute nervousness. I babbled about living in Aldridge near Walsall and explained that I knew he lived in Walsall too. I asked him where, he wasn't comfortable saying precisely where, and when I pushed him to explain exactly where he changed the subject. This was surely a good move on his part since I was coming over as a potential stalker, having told him I thought I'd spotted him a couple of times on The Broadway in Walsall and ludicrously suggesting, "We could meet up for a drink sometime." Where that came from I don't know, I can't explain sometimes what happens in the vaccuum between my brain sending signals and my mouth opening, there seems to be a mischievous interceptor in there determined to make a fool of me. I felt like a prisoner of war tortured by cold showers, sleep deprivation and the exclusion of light. I was disorientated, light headed and sinking fast. Realising my conversation with Tony Rogers was breaking down, he was looking around the room for someone else to talk to, I looked across at Stu to find he was still in earnest conversation with Martin Blunt, they looked very matey.

But then, in a flash, with a mutual brotherly sixth sense, the pair of us noticed that Tim Burgess had broken free of a competition winner and was available for conversation. Abruptly ceasing my conversation with Tony Rogers, to his great relief, I made a beeline for Tim Burgess at the very point that Stu strode across, he too deciding there was bigger fish to fry and cutting Martin Blunt off dead. The three of us met at the same moment, Burgess not knowing which of us to shake hands with first, Stu and I with eyes like saucers and visibly shaking. We were truly in awe. It got off to a bad start, Stu offering his hello at precisely the same time as mine, our greetings clashing. We glared at each other.

Tim Burgess is a quietly spoken, self effacing gentleman. He's shorter than you think he'll be and much less confident too, as he spoke I realised he had not let grandeur of stardom affect him at all, if there was an ego it certainly wasn't in evidence and his warm smile and apparent interest in us was more than we could have expected. He tried to put us at our ease but we weren't able to accept this kind invitation. The nightmare commenced.

" Err... Tim... My kids have drawn a picture for you to sign, I hope you don't mind". I fished out a crumpled pair of coloured drawings that Harry and Hattie had drawn the day before and offered them to him. "One of our favourite songs is A House Is Not A Home and they've tried to depict (I've never used this word before or since) it with these drawings."

He seemed touched if a little bemused and scrawled his autograph plus the words 'GREAT PICTURE'. I muttered nervously that the kids would be pleased but the pleasure was all mine, it wasn't their headboards that these pictures would reside over, it'd be mine. A period of uncomfortable silence followed, so I waded in by talking a little more about this song of theirs. With a hamfisted attempt at suggesting he wrote it in tribute to a Bob Dylan classic "The Ballad Of Frankie Lee & Judas Priest" which contains the line 'It's not a house it's a home,' I instead effectively put forward the case that he'd ripped off Bob Dylan. Burgess looked understandably put out by this assertion and considered his response before replying, giving me enough time to jump in and try and make amends for my mistake. Instead I made it worse.

"Yeah, I know Dylan's a great influence on you, but I know how you like to cut your own path... erm... that's not to say you copied him... .well, maybe borrowed a line... er..."

Stu listened to me digging my hole deeper. I hadn't meant any offence and the words had come out horribly wrong but there was no going back, so I was relieved when he interjected to ask a question of his own in an effort to bail me out. I'd poxed up my big moment, now it was his turn.

"You're going to the States after this show aren't you?" Stu asked. A sensible sentence at last, but he was very nervous in asking it. Stu was shaking and looking to the ceiling, his opening gambit appeared to have drained him of all his energy as he took a long, deep breath having completed his question. Tim Burgess replied that they were heading out in two days time, to which Stu followed up with a question Jeremy Paxman might not wish to claim for his own.

" And how are you getting there?"

Burgess might have smiled or laughed but instead answered earnestly with a straight face, "We're flying". Stu looked at me, I looked at him, he was beetroot red and in shock, had he really asked Tim Burgess how he proposed to get to America? We were making a right horlicks of our big moment but were both so paralysed with stage fright that we felt powerless to do anything about it. Burgess patiently remained standing with us but had now lost all interest in our pathetic conversation. I wasn't finished yet though, there was more.

"It must be a drag performing night after night, bet you're glad this is the last gig of the tour," I said to him. I suppose I asked this in an attempt to gain his confidence, to let him know that it was alright to confide in his new found friends that the tour had been a long, tiring affair and he was relieved it was coming to a conclusion. Instead though, I had greatly offended him.

"No way man. I love performing, love it. Never tire of the rush it gives me, every night's like the first night, I'm always up for it".

He said this while looking deep into my eyes, his face serious now, bare affronted at the suggestion that he may not give his all tonight. I attempted to back out but the damage was done, and it was time for Stu to step in and rescue me.

"I'll take a snap of you both Al, give me the camera." I handed it to him apologetically, conscious he'd been forced to pull me out of the mire. He ushered me closer to Burgess and with the camera raised to his eye, prepared to take a shot. But he couldn't. The camera was in perfect working order, the green light was on, but he was trembling so much that he simply couldn't depress the button with his index finger. The harder he tried the worse it got, the camera shaking under his intense nervousness. I took my turn at bailing him out by pretending the snap had indeed been taken. But Burgess knew the photo hadn't been taken and said so, explaining kindly that he was in no hurry to leave and was prepared to wait while Stu gathered himself. I couldn't stand the pain of all of this though and felt for Stu, so grabbed the camera off him and swapped places so he could stand next to Burgess. Happily my attempt was somewhat more succesful, we now had the photographic evidence to prove Stu had met The Charlatans frontman, Burgess looking relaxed, Stu looking absolutely shell shocked.

The blonde lady who'd greeted us ten minutes prior now re-entered the room and politely told us that the show was over. The band members said their goodbyes and left, Stu and me crashed to the sofa, utterly exhausted by what had just come to pass. In the blink of an eye we'd come, we'd seen, we had far from conquered, and now the room emptied leaving just us, a sniggering barman who'd witnessed our performance with Burgess, and the still becalmed other competition winner. We were invited to grab a free drink before being shooed back into the main hall to mingle with the also rans as they came in to see the show.

It was ages before the show yet and we weren't going to hang around. We couldn't get out of the Academy quick enough, desperately needing fresh air and an opportunity to regroup after the most harrowing of experiences. Once out into the cold night we drank in the piercing air as if it were water in a desert. The debrief started immediately, both of us agreeing on two counts – 1) We had made thorough fools of ourselves and the night had gone worse than we could possibly have imagined, and 2) It was a tremendous relief that this was over. My text to my friend Smithy as we strode back to the car to offload the freebies, pretty well summed up how we both felt – THAT WAS THE MOST TRAUMATIC EVENT OF MY ENTIRE LIFE. And I meant it.

We dumped the posters and CD's in my car, dusted ourselves down, and walked back to the Academy for the gig itself, at a slower speed and in lighter conversation, we were beginning to recover now. I rang Kate to give her a brief description of the events and as I gave her the gory details Stu was laughing, soon so was I, already we were seeing the funny side of our shambolic meeting with The Charlatans. We'd had our chance and we'd blown it. Stu's summary of the whole sorry tale was accurate when he explained we'd attacked this from completely the wrong angle, we should have done just what the other guy had done, shaken hands, taken the autograph, left it there. But we'd wanted the fuller experience, we felt we deserved it as long term fans, so had tried to strike up meaningful conversation and fell flat on our faces. We had embarrased ourselves, but, there were a couple of crumbs of comfort for us both to dwell on. Yes it had been cringeworthy and we'd frozen on our big night, but we'd laugh about this for many a year and while the other competition winner had probably forgotten all about the meeting already, Stu and I had a memory to treasure and share with our friends and family, if treasure were the right word. I wished we could rewind and start again but Stu was right when pointing out it was always going to be like this. Had it been anytime, anywhere, the same would have happened, it was typical of us to have allowed ourselves to have been so gripped with nervousness over something like this and there was an endearing beauty in that. And while we regretted having made arses of ourselves in front of our all time heroes, The Charlatans had forgotten all about us and our hi-jinks from the moment they'd left the room. There was no harm done, only to our egos, and neither of us possessed big egos, it was just us being us. The moral of the story? Don't buy the Walsall Advertiser.

CHAPTER FIFTEEN

"...and I'm finding it so hard to stay in tune..."

Dr Onkawalum, or Dr Dorothy as she's known, studied the small red lesions on my beak. She peered in deep concentration beneath her large framed glasses, her nose screwed up and her mouth gaping open. My nose's blemishes were slight she pointed out, but I'd been conscious of them for four years now and wanted them gone, I'd heard that doctors could perform minor laser surgery these days.

"They are barely visible, why do you want them removed?" she said abruptly.

"They're a permanent reminder of my drinking days. I've read about the skin blistering you get from too much alcohol and this is what's caused them, I'd rather they weren't there," I explained.

"You are right in saying alcohol caused these but I don't understand why you feel they need removing."

"I stopped drinking nearly three years ago, every day's a battle, it doesn't help when I look in the mirror to be reminded how drink has affected me."

"Hmm," replied Dr Dorothy. "Hmm." She had the same expression that my school teachers used to have when I was telling tales that they didn't believe. "Any other reason you'd like me to cost you a lot of money for laser surgery?."

"Well, I suppose there's an element of vanity in there..." I offered meekly.

"Yes! I'm glad you said that and not me. Vanity is the right word. I suggest you turn this on it's head. What is wrong with a reminder of your former life? Would it not strengthen you, protect you from complacency? Wear them like a badge of honour, a milestone of your life past. Rejoice in them," she said triumphantly.

To date, I must confess I hadn't taken the trouble to rejoice in the two red blisters that stuck to the bridge of my nose, no. Any excuse to hold a party and all that, but I struggled to celebrate facial lesions brought on by oceans of Stella Artois. Nevertheless I did find some comfort in what Dr Dorothy said about it being good to have a permanent reminder as a fillip towards me remembering how much better life was since I'd stopped drinking, so I agreed for now to reconsider. She's a feisty lady Dr Dorothy and unless you've got a lot of sound reason you'll struggle to talk her out of a disagreement. My ground was too shaky so I caved in without further ado and whipping off my socks, turned her attention to ailment number two.

"When I take my kids swimming they recoil at the sight of my feet. My toe nails are blacker than the night sky."

Again Dr Dorothy peered beneath her glasses and observed the fearsome fungal explosion that had spread across my toes. "This I am happy to treat," she announced before returning to her seat to type out an instant prescription. She explained I'd need to coat my nails three times a week for as long as six months in order for the fungus to be killed off, the discolouration to grow out and my toes not to frighten my kids anymore. It wasn't just a prescription she issued, I received a sharp lecture too.

"You didn't come last month as I told you. I needed to find out how Christmas went for you and if the tablets were suitable." Her expression had moved on from suspicious school teacher to furious headmaster.

"I had a good Christmas and didn't feel the need to trouble you," I blurted. "If it ain't broke, don't fix it don't they say?" My chuckle didn't impress her.

"I must monitor you closely to give you the right medication. I am glad you feel things are going well but you must involve me in that," she snapped, handing me a green prescription and wishing me a good day. She's a wonderful doctor, Dr Dorothy, a fifty odd year old of Nigerian origin, stern but caring, a doctor who has time for you and doesn't get hung up about keeping you to a ten minute maximum. I've been with her for an hour before now, pouring out my troubles over depression and listening to her best advice as to how I could deal with it in ways other than medication. She believes in medication for depression, but recommends other actions alongside, excercise, sleep, correct eating, that can make a difference and I'm grateful for her advice. Whether the toe tapping patients in the waiting room feel grateful to her as I emerge sixty minutes later is another matter.

What do you do for a living? Are you office based or are you free from the frustrations of a suffocating human sweatbox? I haven't been office based for fifteen years now but haven't forgotten the torment I suffered when sharing a nine to five job with dozens of others who no more wanted to be there than I did. It was bad enough being in a mundane job, form filling and receiving relentless telephone calls to be dealt with in parrot fashion, but worst of all were the abject failures in office etiquette that would have me counting to ten before I lamped someone. Very occasionally these days will I spend a full day in an office environment and it's a stark reminder that were I to drift into office work again some day, my impatience with those around me would see me in possession of a P45 pronto.

The vogue these days is for open plan offices, not the boxed off, individual affairs that people of my father's generation became accustomed to, rows of glass windowed rooms, like an old fashioned train carriage of compartments keeping people apart. Nowadays it's a free for all, vast floors of banked desks littered with telephones, computers and photos of the family. Hot desking is the new thing, nobody 'owns' a desk and can expect it to be waiting for them each time they arrive in the morning, it's first come first served and promotes the mixing of staff as they doss down somewhere differently each day. Well that's the idea, but in reality people get wise and begin to assemble themselves in their favoured positions often enough to suggest they've marked their ground at a particular desk and it's now theirs. Like a dog leaving it's scent, they surreptitiously leave a collection of pens in a personalized pen pot overnight and perhaps a couple of envelopes addressed to them and low and behold, the desk's still vacant when they show up the next day.

And the office comedians I don't miss. I used to travel to work by train, often to be let down by Central Trains' timekeeping, to find myself dashing into the office five minutes late to receive the standard "Good afternoon!" greeting. The old ones aren't the best. And if I left at

4.55pm it'd be, "Just a half day today then is it?" These comedians were normally the chip on the shoulder, world owes them a living type, constantly looking sideways in case someone was enjoying a better deal than them. The sort to return from a week's holiday, open their inbox and announce, "Oh I've got soooo many emails" as if they were soooo important. The fact that 75% of their emails were junk mail and 'straight to delete' office circulars, being neither here nor there to them. And the power trips, oh the power trips, that lasted thousands of miles, until brought to an abrupt halt by bosses who felt their position in the company was threatened by other mortals.

Office geeks were a pain too, blokes with cartoon character ties to suggest they were quite wacky really. Grey suit, plain shirt, but hey, Fred Flinstone is chasing Barney Rubble on my tie so I must be wild. At least though these men could rightfully claim to have adhered to the company dress code. Where was the dress code for women? For men it was suit, shirt, and tie. For women; anything goes. The only time men were given free reign was Comic Relief Day when you're expected to hold a sensible work related conversation with someone dressed up like Widow Twankey while you're parading around the office with your underpants worn the wrong side of your trousers.

Of course PA's were beyond all of this. As right hand ladies to the decision makers of the business, the head honchos who stand up at corporate conferences to bore you rigid while you make paper aeroplanes with the agenda, they strutted around the office as if they owned the place. A protective glow enveloped them, the great untouchables PA's were, bullet proof because they had the ear and confidence of the boss. Though they were clearly faultless in every regard, they didn't see the virtue of humility as an edifying option, so their noses remained either high in the air as they flounced around the office or somewhere near the boss's backside. I didn't cross them, they were like children to the executives and acted as such when running to them to tell tales. I kept my distance and my gossip from them.

The benefit however of PA's was that their general attitude and surliness often meant they didn't converse with you. This silence was a welcome contrast to the guff spouted by colleagues who took it in turns to audition for village idiot status. I'm talking about the ceaseless repetition of television catchphrases that last the course until the new one comes along. Just as, "I don't believe it" by would-be Victor Meldrews was finally shelved after a year's use, along came "Suits you Sir," or "Loadsamoney". Harry Enfield had a lot to answer for. These people were able to take a classic series, say The Office, and regurgitate the script so often that I ended up hating a show I used to love. And there were the armchair football fans who hadn't been to a match since Bobby Charlton played, but ripped into me when Villa lost at the weekend. They had absolutely no right, especially if the match they were referring to was one I had driven a 400 mile round trip to the bleak north to see. One guy I remember in particular would joyfully give it laldy about my beloved team's shortcomings yet the only effort he'd make to watch his own team was to occasionally raise his head out of his front room chicken chow mein, after his Saturday night skinful, to catch snippets of Albion's latest defeat on Match Of The Day.

But who was worse? The aforementioned footballing guru or the mobile phone irritant? There are certainly far more of the latter. Where do you start with these people? Their ring tones, I've had serious telephone conversations interrupted by a mobile phone going off at the next desk with "I Like To Move, It Move It" playing full tilt, while it's owner is in the kitchen making a brew. He's not there to switch his phone off, I can't reach, so the customer on my telephone line continues his earnest speech about our lack of customer service while serenaded by Reel 2 Real. Not that the absence of the mobile phone owner is the main problem, more often than not it's their presence. Ever tried to get on with your work while a colleague, usually male, answers his mobile and in an instant becomes oblivious to where he is and who's around him? He'll get to his feet, leave his desk, and circle a patch of floor just a few yards away as he bellows into his phone, the rest of the office benefiting from the details of his weekend, his last round of golf and the state of his marriage. We may also benefit from the sight of him picking his arse by the photocopier, smoothing his hair in the reflection offered by the window or delving a finger into his nostril. Mobile phones are dangerous. Not just in respect of their use by motorists but more so because of their propensity to lure people into revealing secrets that they'd otherwise never reveal. If you want to unearth private information out of a man here's a plan; put a mobile phone in his hand, get his best friend to telephone him at work, and ask a colleague of his to lend an ear to the conversation. He won't have to listen hard, the bloke will sing like a canary and hey presto, the truth is out. Text messaging can be a problem too, I told my boss I loved him once when pressing 'send' at the wrong time.

I remember too the 'walk of death'. You know how it is; you enter a long, empty, doorless corridor and begin the walk to the double doors at the other end. There's nobody around until the doors at the opposite end fling open and there enters Paula, the battleaxe of the office, happy with nothing in life other than the sound of her own voice, forever grumbling about the corporate and wider world. You've had a run in with her recently and told her to belt up, she's gone to the boss and lodged a formal complaint. You now have thirty silent seconds to think of something to say as she approaches, clasping her files close to her chest and walking at pace. She walks in a straight line, eyes fixed front, pretending you're not there, you shuffle along, nervously running your hand through your hair and as you meet in the middle it's the moment of truth. You begin a mumbled "Hello", but she steams ahead, as if you didn't exist. I used to have no end of these awkward moments and never got comfortable dealing with them. Walking into a lift that someone had let one go in was a common problem too, very embarrassing when it stops at the next floor and someone else walks in thinking you're the one who dropped it.

Yes, all things considered, I'm decided that an office job will never be for me and I say this for the sake of potential colleagues and my family as much as myself. It would be the end of me as a sane person. Instead I'll continue to pound the roads of the Midlands, visiting customers, drinking their tea and hopefully obtaining their autographs on bank documentation. It has its drawbacks being a 'location independent worker', you can get very lonely after two days of no customer appointments and just yourself for company. The walls at chez Russon have been climbed many times as my paperwork has dried up and there are no customers ready to see me, I'm not the greatest when on my own, it's not long before a dark cloud hones into view and empties itself over me, although since Emily came along and with Kate on maternity leave, it isn't often that I'm home alone anymore.

Driving so many miles as a travelling salesman is something that has never got me down, it's got me into trouble, but never got me down. And it's changed me as a driver. In the early days I was something of a hothead behind the wheel, never slow to sound my horn and offer hand signals to motorists who had cut me up, or not indicated as they turned, or jumped a red light, or parked themselves in the middle lane, or driven too slowly, you name it. But I've mellowed and finally accepted that there are no perfect drivers out there, except perhaps me, and if I were to allow myself to become irritated with their every shortcoming, I may as well leave my horn sounding permanently. I just smile these days when I'm cut up, and laugh at the laziness of non-indicators. Middle lane sitters I'm still working on. And tailgaters.

CHAPTER SIXTEEN

"... a chance to start again and wipe the slate..."

Despite an improvement in discipline, St Thomas had managed to accumulate enough points to be called to a Disciplinary Hearing by the WMCFL. A recent red card and a couple of yellows had tipped us over the edge and a meeting was set at The Drake's Drum, a boozer in Great Barr, where in an upstairs room we were to be taken to task by the league committee.

The manager wasn't permitted to attend this hearing since he was a member of the committee himself, so volunteers were sought to bend over and take six of the best. Possibly because my hide is sturdier than most in the team, I was 'volunteered' along with our captain, Joe Lister. Champions League football was resuming that same evening and it meant I'd miss Man United's trip to Lille, but having little time for United and the fortunes thereof, I was happy to shuffle along to The Drake's Drum and represent the team instead. Rob dropped off some papers to prepare me for the meeting, I sat down to read them the night before. Never having been presented with WMCFL written correspondence, I felt quite important leafing though the papers, rather like Judge John Deed as he presides over a case of the realm, I didn't bother with the wig though.

The letter calling us to the hearing was accompanied by copies of previous disciplinary correspondence and the recent referee's report regarding Ian Pearsall's sending off which I began to read before spluttering over my coffee as I reached the nuts and bolts of it. Ian had apparently displayed a limited vocabulary of about five expletives... .

"... in the 79th minute I turned to follow the ball and heard a shout of "F*** off". I stopped the game and consulted with my assistant. He confirmed to me that these words had been shouted. I dismissed the player from the field of play. After he left the field he continued swearing in a very threatening manner, saying, "f*** off you c***... .."

I hadn't realised officials gave an account of events verbatim, I'd assumed they'd simply provide the general gist without specifics, not being overly graphic. I flicked over to read the linesman's account of events, it got worse...

"...the referee asked me if I could identify a player who had shouted "F*** off". I said that I could and pointed the player out at which point he came charging towards me shouting various foul language before being restrained and escorted away by team mates. When play moved up by the dugout he again started verbally abusing me "Knob head, bald headed little b*****d etc."

I asked the player to leave the dugout, he said, "Are you going to f***ing make me you bald headed b*****d," and made threats that he would sort me out after the game." I made the referee aware of this situation and the player was asked to return to the dressing room."

I remember this incident very well. I was in the dugout at the time, having been substituted, and saw it all unfold at close proximity. Unfortunately these reports accurately reflected what had happened and weren't a pleasant reminder. Ian had been out of order that morning and he knew it, he couldn't be more apologetic after the game, but the damage was done and we as a club now faced the consequences. You had to feel for the linesman that day, a guy with a few years under his belt, running the line because of his love of parks football and being summarily abused as a reward for his commitment, it wasn't on.

Tonight's hearing wasn't solely regarding Ian's sending off but rather the accumulated disciplinary points gathered by the team as a whole, Nick Jones not being unselfish with his share of five bookings. I anticipated however that the hearing would centre around Ian's two sendings off this season and had prepared my defence accordingly, assuming of course I were to receive the opportunity to speak. Not having been to one of these do's before, the committee may simply bring down the hammer after dishing out a rollicking and that would be that, I'd be back home in time for the Nine O'clock News. I expected though that Joe and I would be given the floor at some stage, and decided that when it was my turn to speak, I'd talk about the reparation we were trying to make concerning Ian.

It would have been easy to jettison the guy from the team, tell him he wasn't wanted and not to darken our door again. Excellent player though he was, he could be a liability with his poor discipline and propensity to blow up at a moment's notice, normally over nothing in particular. Part of the problem may have been due to his great ability as a footballer, he was clearly playing at a level in the WMCFL, that was some way below him and the frustration that this can bring had surely been a factor in his behaviour. Good players with poorer ones around them can become exasperated as their measured passes aren't anticipated by team mates or their clever running into space not rewarded with the ball to their feet. Not just that, they must shake their heads in despair as they watch carthorses like me fail to pass the ball, preferring instead to wallop it off the pitch and into the stratosphere when under no pressure from the opposition. Dribbling? I couldn't beat an egg. Scoring? I couldn't finish a bag of crisps. Ian's frustration was understandable, though he never verbalised it so I may have been off the mark with this assumption, but regardless, it didn't condone his actions. But we liked him, respected him as a footballer, and understood what a positive influence in his life being part of a football team was. He loved playing football and we wanted to continue to give him that opportunity, this was to be my opening salvo to the committee.

Second, and more importantly as far as I could see, we had to have room for forgiveness in our football team and in this football league. It had come to a pretty pass if a Christian football team wasn't able to forgive one of it's players for misbehaviour and support them as they strove to make amends. Rob Hill, Rich Taylor and I had discussed this and prayed for Ian, and all members of our football team, that whatever they faced in life and wherever their lives had taken them, the football team might represent a safe haven for them to return to twice a week for camaraderie and fellowship. I hoped very much that the league committee would agree.

Joe picked me up and we discussed our plan of attack as we drove. It became clear that he too had identified that if Nick and Ian were to straighten themselves out, we as a team would have no major disciplinary problem, and this is what we needed to put across to the committee. Parking alongside the only other two cars in the pub's vast car park, we headed solemnly to the gallows. In truth, I think we both expected that this would be a low key, 'quiet chat and be on your way' type affair, not an arm around the shoulder job, but a convivial conversation where we'd be told politely to get our house in order, we'd humbly accept and return home within the hour. This was not to be the case.

The bar was virtually empty, just a couple of lads playing pool in front of a huge screen showing the Man United game. Joe and I ordered drinks and explained to the barmaid why we were there, she kindly lead us through to the lounge via the back of the bar. A strange feeling that, every pub you ever go in has a sacrosanct area that must not be entered, the other side of the bar, but she had no qualms about taking us through, she could see our pockets weren't large enough to stash away more than a packet of dry roasted. Through to the lounge, up the darkened stairs and into the dank, miserable surroundings of an ill-lit function suite where we were greeted by the three members of the disciplinary committee, Tony Skelton (Disciplinary Officer), James Oratayo (Fixtures Secretary) and Richard Webster (Minutes Secretary). They were sat next to each other in front of a row of hastily assembled tables, two seats had been set out for us opposite, also in front of tables, and the two parties faced each other from a distance of about four yards.

Tony introduced himself and the two members of the committee that flanked him, before inviting us to announce who we were. He then turned immediately to the matter in hand, explaining in no uncertain terms how disappointed the committee was in the behaviour this season of St Thomas. With a couple of clubs out of the twenty in the league showing a completely unblemished record and most of the others accumulating very few points, our name stuck out like a sore thumb in the indiscipline rankings and they expected some action. With 25 points now having been reached (if only we could have had that tally in the league table proper), we found ourselves in hot water, another five points however and it would be scalding, a heavy fine and possible expulsion. This pulled Joe and I up sharp, we had no idea that we were this close to serious repercussion. We shut up and kept listening.

The points system was explained to confirm how we'd managed to reach 25 and a breakdown of the culprits handed to us, Joe looking slightly sheepish when finding his name on there, he'd received his solitary booking the same day Ian was sent off. This breakdown again showed Nick and Ian top of the hit parade with 18 points between them. We were rightly reminded that this was a Christian league with a very good reputation that the committee had no desire for us to sully. Joe intervened to ask for clarification on the points system since some bookings appeared to warrant one point, while others gave two or even three, this was duly explained, foul and abusive language giving more points than persistent fouling for instance, and then it was over to us to answer Tony's question, "What assurances can you give the committee that action will be taken to deal with your poor disciplinary record, and what in particular will you be doing differently to improve matters?"

Joe spoke first after a steadying gulp of coke, confirming that one of the players, Nick Jones, had already made amends for early season indiscipline and had only received one booking in recent weeks. Added to this he'd already found himself before the committee a couple of weeks prior having reached five bookings for the season and confirmed directly to them that he intended to finish the season without a further booking. He'd been contrite and the committee acknowledged and welcomed this.

It was then onto the subject of Ian, I chose to butt in. I got off to a hesitant start, unaccustomed to having a disciplinary panel staring at me and measuring my every word and after a few sentences, I felt like asking them if I could come in and start again. Tongue tied, dry mouthed and fidgeting in my seat, I looked every inch the guilty culprit being interrogated by Inspector Morse, and as such, I babbled like one. I eventually found my feet and explained how we took the situation with Ian very seriously and wanted very much to rectify matters, not by dispensing with him, but by working with him and praying for him. As a Christian team in a Christian league we felt strongly that there should be the offer of forgiveness and an opportunity for Ian to be supported by the rest of the team in his efforts to mend his ways. Perhaps there would come a time when we all agreed it just wasn't working and a further decision needed to be made then, but for now, we hoped that our prayers and support for Ian would be accepted by the league.

This drew agreement from the committee but still there was the feeling from them that we were being unrealistic in expecting not to reach the 30 point mark by the season's end and face a fine, or possible expulsion. They wanted further confidence in us and asked what other practical steps we would be taking to address matters. Joe and I looked at each other for inspiration, our well appeared to have run dry way too early in proceedings. Our proposed defence had been well planned but not our remedial action. Feeling hot under the collar and perhaps wishing two other volunteers may have been found for tonight, the pair of us took time to assemble our individual thoughts before blurting out pretty much the same idea; Joe, as captain, would call order in the dressing room before Saturday's game and explain the importance of keeping our discipline. I piped up that I too would be happy to say a few words, and rather than leave it to our manager to read the riot act all the time, perhaps we should take more accountability ourselves as senior members of the team.

The committee were happy with this suggestion but explained that it was no good doing this once, we needed to be carrying out a pre-match pep talk on discipline every week. They weren't letting us off lightly at all, Joe and I were starting to sweat, I'd finished my pint of orange ages ago, I normally nurse it for an hour but kept swigging from it tonight, in apprehension. We agreed that a regular reminder to the players was needed, and a further conversation with Nick and Ian called for. The seven week ban that Ian was about to embark on would however disenable him from collecting any more points unless he managed to get sent off from the sidelines, (something that we couldn't altogether rule out).

We sat back having ended the case for the defence, Tony Skelton observing us while stroking his chin. He didn't give much away, neither did his cohorts, but I was comfortable that our approach had shown them that we were taking this issue seriously, far more seriously to be honest than we were doing before we arrived tonight. They'd shaken us up with the earnest nature in which they'd dealt with this hearing and we needed this if we were to make genuine attempts at righting the ship of discipline that was currently heading for the rocks. After a few words from James Orayoto and Richard Webster, putting their opinions forward on how we might sort matters out, Tony asked that we put into practice, immediately, all that we'd suggested, he also explained that we'd be receiving further correspondence in the post as to what punishment the committee had decided upon as a result of tonight's hearing. We thanked them for their time, got up and got out, desperate for air after the stifling atmosphere in this darkest of function suites. I wouldn't be recommending to Kate that Emily's christening reception should be held there. We staggered to the car, with whiter complexions than when we'd arrived. Joe drove us home, preparing his speech for Saturday as he went.

The following day I gave up tea & coffee for lent. I also added 'the attendance of disciplinary hearings' to the list of items I'd avoid. It had been far from a pleasant experience, though conversely one that I was glad I'd gone through. The committee had been stark, true and fair and their manner had brought home to us that our ill discipline couldn't continue if we were to remain a respected part of the league, or potentially even remain part of the league at all. It was heartening to see how much the committee cared for this league and took it seriously, its reputation they were very proud of and keen to protect and it was good to feel part of such an organisation. A couple of days later came the written confirmation that we had brought the league into disrepute, were to be warned as to our future conduct and fined £50. It was also brought to our attention that should we reach the 30 disciplinary points mark, it was possible we wouldn't have a club anymore. The goal for the remainder of our season was now twofold; to gain promotion and to ensure we still had a club able to take its place in the first division once that promotion had been gained.

CHAPTER SEVENTEEN

"… we're together, on our way…"

When I played for St Mary's, we were terrible in the early days, terrible with a capital T. Each week we'd find ourselves on the end of a sound thrashing and when we managed the occasional draw, it was celebrated as if it were a victory. We shared bottom spot throughout the season with the second of Chawn Hill's teams, they had one in each division then, and vied with them for the wooden spoon year on year. Invariably we'd escape this disgrace, scrambling just enough points to leave them rooted, that to us was success. But after a couple of consecutive seasons hacking around in the bowels of the second division, the worm began to turn. A few fresh faces were introduced, a larger squad encouraged competition for places and gradually defeats became draws and draws became victories. A season later we had hauled ourselves up into mid-table, consolidated, and a couple of years later, gained promotion.

St Boniface, our opponents today, reminded me of an early day St Mary's. Without being unkind, they'd been considered whipping boys since their introduction to the league, they'd admit this themselves, they'd have to, and teams expected to inflict a comprehensive hiding upon them time after time. But recent weeks had seen an improvement, new players had been brought in, and while they were still losing matches, it was only narrowly and against good opposition. We turned up at their ground to play our first game of football in three weeks and were reminded by our manager that this was not a team to underestimate, they were no longer a pushover, and as the game progressed we found this to be very much the truth.

A familiar face to Joe Lister and myself greeted us as we walked from the car park to the portakabin changing rooms. It was Tony Skelton, the league disciplinary officer, who'd decided to see at first hand just how serious St Thomas were taking the midweek dressing down he'd delivered. He informed us that he'd be addressing our players in the dressing room fifteen minutes before kick-off if we'd be so kind as to ensure the team were assembled. I was pleased about this. Joe had intended to speak, and this he later did, but to have Tony putting us straight over our disciplinary record at first hand was going to carry an even greater impact. We agreed to be ready for him at the appointed time, but first needed to establish that the game was going ahead. Overnight rain had turned the pitch into a mud heap and the opposing team's manager was furiously pushing water uphill in the six yard box with only a sweeping brush to help him. It seemed futile, it was quite frankly, but at least it intimated to the referee, inspecting the pitch a few yards away, that there was a determination for this match to be staged. To hammer this home, the St Boniface players draped nets over goalposts and splashed through the mud to spear the corner flags into the four corners of the pitch. There's a lot of kidology that goes on in situations like this, I'm sure the refs have seen it all before, but as players we believe we're doing a number on referees with this sort of persuasion, it probably makes not a jot of difference but makes us feel better.

Around 20% of the pitch could claim to be grass covered, the remainder being a combination of small puddles, cowhouse mud and a terrain better suited to stock car racing. But we weren't complaining, we just wanted to play football and once the go ahead was given, we were straight off to the bleak, graffiti strewn portakabin to get changed. There's rarely room to swing a cat in these changing rooms, arses are shoved into faces as players get changed, elbows dig into your ribs, it's great at building team togetherness. Clem got changed in the showers because there was no room for him to perch his backside in the changing area, and that's with only twelve players present, how a full complement would get changed together in there I don't know, they must do it in shifts. No harm done though, we're there to play football not luxuriate in sprawling carpeted dressing rooms, we leave that to the prima donnas of the Premiership after they've parked their Chelsea tractors and Porsches in club car parks with supporters pressing their faces up against caged fencing which further widens the gap between fans and players. It used to be the game of the people, not anymore.

Joe Lister had taken a blow to his eye in training through the week, Matt Brady managing to gouge his captain's eye during an entanglement, and he'd suffered blurred vision ever since. He'd see a specialist on Monday but had come along to support his charges and deliver the disciplinary talk that he'd promised Tony at the hearing. It's difficult quietening down a room full of hairy arsed guys getting themselves ready for battle and exhibiting the type of childish knockabout buffoonery you see in most dressing rooms. It can be a lonely place standing there, pontificating to the team, waiting for the rise to be taken out of you for being such a ponce for talking about naughtiness on the football field, but Joe carried out his duty manfully. He was immediately followed by Tony Skelton, who laid it on on the line, starkly bringing home the gravity of our situation – "30 points and you face expulsion, you're on 25 and there's still six games left, think about it". Looking around the team I prayed the penny had now dropped.

With kick-off only ten minutes away, a couple of the players searched in vain for a throne to park their porous backsides upon, but the toilets were locked, last night's Indian takeaway was going to have to remain within them for a couple of hours more. Valuables, as always, were placed in a sports bag for Rob to look after at pitchside, you never know whether the changing rooms are going to be locked behind you, safer to put your clothes in your car and your personal belongings in Rob's 'valuables' bag. You can sue him if anything goes missing. Then it was the long walk to the pitch, a good hundred yards from the dressing rooms. Playing at Selly Oak playing fields is a far cry from having the Champions League anthem bugle the teams from their cosy dressing rooms, along a polished floor and through a cosseting tunnel onto the pitch to present themselves before an adoring audience. We don't hold hands with mascots in this league and we don't form a line to shake hands politely with the opposition who privately we're hoping to batter. Instead we drift slowly in ones ond twos from a portakabin, across a car park where we dump our belongings in the car, and amble nonchalantly to a football pitch that doubles through the week as a dog littering arena and home for winos.

The pitch was set to the left hand side of a vast playing field, a couple of dozen schoolkids trained on the adjacent one in their football kits from around the globe, sadly failing to represent local football, all

Man United, Chelsea and Real Madrid from what I could see. I blamed the parents. When my son Harry came home from school at the age of 7 announcing that his friends supported Man United and he was going to as well, I marched him up to the Villa club shop, bought a replica shirt and had his name printed on the back. He was a Villa fan and that was that, he'd thank me for it in later life (!).

The sprinkling of spectators were outnumbered on this greyest of grey days by the half dozen oak trees that towered some way behind our goal. I wondered how many nightmare amateur football matches they must have witnessed over the years, it was a wonder they hadn't died. The pre-match warm up was organised properly, Matt Brady leading the merry dance from touchline to touchline, knees up, back flicks and shoulder rolling, it looked pretty professional until one of our number slipped in the mud and crashed to the floor. Aware that Tony Skelton was amongst the spectators, we vowed to honour his pre-match plea regarding discipline as we huddled together to talk tactics. This didn't take long. Tactics at our level are forgotten the moment the match kicks off so we choose not to bother with any apart from the routine, "Get your foot in early, let 'em know you're there," type stuff. And then we were off.

We couldn't have started in better fashion, Mark Hadden notching the opening goal after two minutes following an 'after you Claude' mix up between their keeper and centre back. Five minutes later though, our first and only substitution was enforced (we only had twelve players available today) when Chris Preece hobbled off with a thigh strain taking his leather driving gloves with him. He always wears gloves on the pitch for some reason, peculiar for a tall rugged centre back, but at least they're usually woolly ones. Today he looked like Leslie Phillips in his gleaming, black leather gauntlets, better suited when accompanied by a waistcoat and a monacle rather than a mud spattered football shirt. Clem slotted into Chris's central defensive position alongside me, the Abbot & Costello of amateur football defending reforming after a season together at the back with St Mary's four years ago.

Slide tackling was a must on this surface. If a defender didn't relish these conditions he had no right to call himself a defender at all. I managed a couple of spectacular ten yard slides, one that took ball and man and one which saw me miss both and slide out of play as the game went on behind me, very embarrassing. This was somewhat usurped by a Chris Rogers slide tackle later in the game which was abruptly halted after two yards as he glided into a puddle and sat upright with water lapping around him, looking like an abandoned toddler sat in a dirty nappy. Sensible play would have seen us attempting to switch the ball to the grassier bits on the flanks but once the whistle goes, it's heads down, kick and rush football at this level and basic common sense, such as getting the ball out of the mud, flies out of the window.

It was one all after twenty minutes, St Boniface converting a boggy goalmouth scramble after a corner hadn't been cleared but before long we re-established our lead with Mark Hadden heading in a rebound off the crossbar. It remained 2-1 until half-time but within ten minutes of the resumption St Boniface had equalised once more with the sort of goal Alan Hansen would be having kittens over. As their left winger approached the penalty box on our right hand side, three of our four defenders, myself included, left our stations to be drawn across to him, leaving just poor old Daz to mark three St Boniface players as they stormed into the box to receive the cross. When it came over they formed a queue to slot the ball home from ten yards and our kamikaze defending found us on level terms again. If Alan Hansen wasn't there to have kittens, Chris Preece was, our substituted hand muff wearing centre back lashing out from the sidelines and quite rightly so. When you're on the field of play you can feel the team is fairly well organised and performing adequately, when you're looking on from the sidelines as Chris now was, it becomes clear just how ineptly the team is in fact performing. The hiders and the lightweights are easily spotted, the lack of pace from older players laid bare for all to see, and comical defending strikes you right between the eyes. At our level, you're not expecting a whole lot of skill but you do demand one hundred percent effort in a 'blood and snotters' operation to outfight your opposition. We were beginning to allow St Boniface to outmuscle us and for a fifteen minute spell after they scored, it appeared there'd only be one winner until we began taking a foothold in the game, well, as firm as a foot could be held on this nightmare surface.

Both teams slogged it out in the increasingly boggy conditions, straining for every tackle in the mud, but it seemed that we wanted the winning goal slightly more than they did. Where they'd be comfortable with a draw, a sign of another step forward in their progress, we knew that only a win would do to maintain our promotion challenge. And while they were so used to losing that they now wanted simply to protect a draw, we were desperate to convert one point to three. We entered the final five minutes on the back of sustained pressure and it was then that Matt Brady was tripped in the box, fell face down in a puddle of mud, and Mark Hadden had the responsibility of the resultant penalty kick. At times like this I'm happy to be a shrinking violet. Given a list of volunteers to take a late penalty to secure victory, I would be found somewhere around ten or eleven, fighting out last spot with the keeper. I admire people who take responsibility, put their hand up and their head above the parapet if that's not too many cliches in one sentence. Today Mark was the man, keen to upgrade his two goal salvo to a headline grabbing hat-trick, and while St Boniface's players berated the referee for giving the penalty, Mark gathered himself in preparation. Once the squabbling between outraged St Boniface players and elated St Thomas ones ended, it was time for Mark to step up for his attempt at glory and like an Alan Shearer of yesteryear, he duly creamed the ball into the top corner with the keeper diving the other way. He charged towards the corner flag in celebration, Mark not the keeper, and began some sort of samba dance. A couple of team mates who'd set off in pursuit to share the delirium of the moment, thought better of it once they saw his ridiculous jig and not wishing to identify themselves with this daft herbert now limbo dancing on a grey day in Selly Oak, they trotted solemnly back to the halfway line. It was a few embarrassing seconds later before Mr Hadden turned around to find he was celebrating alone, the rest of the team had returned to their mark for the resumption.

The game petered out from there except for one firm header upon our goal which our keeper, Rob Woods, dealt with. A valuable three points had been earned against a team I believed and hoped would be fighting for promotion themselves next season. We couldn't wait to learn about the results of the teams around us. Once they were in, the league table read as follows, with just five games remaining of our season and three teams to be promoted –

	Played	Points
Rowley College	10	28
City Church	12	27
Us	13	25
Zion Athletic	14	23
Dynamo Kingswinford	11	22
Halesowen Zion	11	21
Selly Oak Methodist	13	8
Brierley Hill AOG	10	5
St Boniface	12	5
Walsall Olympic	12	2

CHAPTER EIGHTEEN

"... take the straight line, feel the sunshine..."

Alcohol and substance misuse. Not a happy subject, not a happy life, but having gone three years without a drink, after eighteen years swilling gallons of it, I decided it was time to enroll on an outbound course run by Gloucester University and Life For The World Trust. It's full title 'Alcohol & Substance Misuse Counselling Certificate'. Well, professional footballers are always being urged to 'put something back into the community' aren't they? I thought I'd take a leaf out of their book and try to give something to my community, earn a qualification and look forward to helping out others in the pit of alcoholic despair.

I'd become aware of this course thanks to Caz Hill at St Thomas Church. She works with young people, many of whom have problems with drink and drugs, and had given me details of an organisation called Life For The World Trust. They're a Christian organisation, based in Bath, who dedicate their efforts to dealing with people in addiction. The course was part time, I needed to travel to Derby to attend it once a fortnight, and the enrolment was today.

I felt pretty emotional as I set off from home for the first day. Normally I'd have Five Live on the radio or music playing, but for once I drove in silence, thinking about the course, thinking about why I was doing it. My thoughts turned to Peter, the counsellor who'd become my friend during his long, laboured work with me. And I thought too about what had brought me to him in the first place, was I really an alcoholic? Did life really become unmanageable? It had been so long ago, that my memories of the despair had drifted away, and it's at times like this that alcoholics become complacent and begin to believe they could return to drinking and be able to manage it, control it. But they can't, I can't, it controls you, you don't control it, I had to remind myself of that every day.

How bad had it got for me? Try turning up for meetings drunk, waking up in the morning under a hedge or on a park bench, cancelling access to my children because of desperate hangovers, ruining people's weddings and parties making a drunken spectacle of myself, missing my Granny's memorial service because a drinking session the night before rendered me incapable, ruining good friendships by becoming intolerably arrogant and foolish when drunk, throwing up on the last bus or train too many times to remember. And what about the missed opportunities. Attending the British Open Golf Championships to be drunk by 9am and spend the remainder of the day alone in a beer tent, travelling to Villa away games but staying in the pub by the ground while friends left for the match, holidaying in beautiful parts of the world only to stay poolside every day to get sloshed rather than take in the sights, passing up job opportunities because I was too drunk to attend the interview, the list goes on.

So many, many times I've spoiled events for others and myself by being drunk, but the pain isn't purely in that, when you're a drinker you don't even notice. The real pain is the feeling of guilt, despair and shame. You hate yourself for drinking but you keep doing it. You get down so you get drunk and the vicious circle continues. The number of times I've drank alone far outweighs the drinking sessions with mates, the Friday nights out and entire weekends on the lash. Countless times I've sat alone at home in the morning, cracked open a tin of beer and ploughed on from there until I can't focus anymore. Waking up with a hangover, I'd 'cure' myself by getting straight back onto the beer to recreate the woozy feeling that deadened my thoughts and shut out the world. My whole life was punctuated by drink. Something to celebrate? Let's have a drink. Feeling fed up? Let's have a drink. Bored? Go down the pub and have a drink. Alcohol was at the centre of all I did. I managed to hold down a job because I worked in sales and could organise my diary to fit around my drinking, though very often I cancelled appointments because I was drunk, getting drunk or hungover. So much of my time was spent in my 'home office', speaking to customers on the telephone, they couldn't see me in my jeans, in front of the telly, swigging from a can of Stella. It was easy. Only occasionally did I have to shape up and keep the head, stay sober to attend an important meeting or a family function. I became an expert in disguising the fact that I was an alcoholic. My children, Harry and

Hattie never saw me drink but never knew how many times I was hungover and firing on no cylinders when I had them.

I'd had several aborted attempts at sobriety, including one that lasted five months. I remember telling the world I'd cracked it, I even wrote a book about it, but this turned out to be a foolhardy decision as it heaped pressure on me to continue abstinence and before long I was back where I started, lost in alcohol. But then, after eighteen years of drinking, the last four as a helpless alcoholic, matters came to a crunch. On March 8th 2004 I was at home, alone, sat at my desk in the front room of my small terraced house in Walsall. My laptop was on, The Charlatans were playing Us & Us Only on the stereo, I was working. With no appointments that day, I'd wandered downstairs early and started on my paperwork. The bank love their paperwork, so I was filling in forms, sending emails and generally clearing the decks. At around 10.30am I fetched a can of Stella out of the fridge and returned to my desk. A few minutes later I returned for another one, this time bringing the rest of the four pack with me. By lunchtime they'd all gone and I was singing with The Charlatans at the top of my voice. I'd switched off my mobile and I'd completed my work, each entry on my day books list of tasks had been crossed out with satisfied strokes of my marker pen.

It was a rotten day outside, the rain pelting down and a gusty wind driving it into the faces of people as they passed my front window, their collars pulled up, their shoulders hunched. But I was going to have to join them, I'd run out of beer, so I walked to the carry out a few minutes away and re-stocked. By mid afternoon I'd finished off these cans too and began to think about what to do next. I had no work pressing, I had no plans to meet Kate that afternoon (we didn't live together, we'd not long been seeing each other), I had no plans for the rest of the day at all. So I decided a one-man pub crawl was in order and I started with the The Spring Cottage, a typically ugly and old fashioned boozer a five minute walk away. I reached there around 3.30 and sat alone at the bar, nursing a pint of Kronenbourg and deciding between Scampi Fries or pork scratchings. There were no other customers, the barman was sorting a delivery in the cellar, the television was off. I looked around to find myself sitting in an empty pub, in silence, very much alone. It troubled me.

From there I walked to The Poacher's Pocket, a good ten minutes away. I wasn't staggering, I'd drank a lot but over a long period, and although I was full of alcohol, I'd levelled off in the last couple of hours. Cars whizzed by, and heavy goods vehicles on the busy Lichfield Road sprayed me with water. I didn't care, I was in a world of my own. I arrived at The Poacher's Pocket hoping for a warmer atmosphere than The Spring Cottage but found it just as depressing. Two uniformed bar staff chatted over mugs of tea at the end of the bar, not breaking their conversation as one of them served me. Apart from acknowledging my finger jabbing at the Grolsch pump, I may as well have been invisible to them. Money was taken and change given without eye contact or verbal interaction. I went and sat in the corner. Again, I was the only customer in there, accompanied by two bar staff and a Karaoke guy setting up his gear for the evening, it was 5pm. They went about their business oblivious to my existence and once again I stared at my glass feeling beaten. This was a soul-less place, not decrepit like the last pub, but a clean, plastic, darkened Irish theme pub kind of place that sold food. Not a proper pub. I finished my pint and moved on.

The Four Crosses was an acquired taste. A real drinker's pub. No meals, no children, no lounge, clean, tidy, but not overly welcoming. It had a number of hardened regulars, mostly middle aged men and women. You went there to drink. I walked in to be greeted by a moody, Bett Lynch kind of character behind the bar, who treated me with disdain, I assumed because I wasn't a regular. I ordered a pint of Carling, I couldn't handle any more strong lager, and troughed into a bag of cheese & onion. Bett Lynch looked at me long and hard, suspiciously. I knew how drunk I was and struggled now to hide it, my eyes were seeing double and she was clearly in two minds whether to serve me. She lifted her eyebrows as she gave me the change as if to say, 'Think yourself lucky I've served you but you ain't gettin' another.' I shuffled to the wooden bench opposite the long, narrow, brightly lit bar and sat down.

There were two workmen sat on bar stools, deep in animated conversation. It was all very convivial, not at all threatening, they were in a world of their own as their heightened voices exchanged heated opinion. The rest of the bar was empty and the barmaid had gone out the back somewhere, so this was now the third straight pub I'd come to where there wasn't a hint of conversation for me to engage in and where I'd been left to feel pretty pathetic, a thirty three year old man, sitting in a bar, drunk and alone. I felt extremely lonely.

I was struggling to get any more drink down me by now and nursed my pint for a good half hour before getting anywhere near the bottom of the glass. Fiddling with my coat pocket zip, I realised I'd brought my mobile phone with me but not switched it on yet. I turned it on and looked at it willing a text message to appear from someone, anyone, but there was nothing. The loneliness became overwhelming for a minute or two, so I texted a couple of friends to ask them if they fancied joining me for a drink. Dan said he'd be there to collect me in half an hour, Nick said he'd meet me in The Elms at 8pm. Drinkers like company, it normalises their behaviour when others are joining them.

Dan was the only other customer to arrive since I had, the pub remained almost empty. He ordered a soft drink and sat next to me, realising something was amiss straight away. I'd invited him along so we could share a few pints and a laugh, but he was clearly in no mood. He hadn't come to drink, he'd come on a rescue mission. Dan's a gentle and quiet guy, he loves a session just like most men, but he also cares for his friends and appreciated tonight wasn't the night to be partying.

"How long you been 'ere?" He looked directly into my eyes.

"Dunno mate, an hour or so"

"And where've you been up to now?"

I answered him honestly but not with bravado, I felt ashamed recanting the day's events where normally I'd consider it some sort of badge of honour drinking for such a sustained period.

"You don't need any more mate," he said.

"We're meeting Sprason at eight," I replied.

"We still can, but you don't need any more." Dan left it at that and we continued talking, I can't remember what about, probably football knowing us, but his point had been made. His reaction to me had a big effect. He'd told me once before what an arse I could be when I was drunk, I'd laughed it off but he wasn't laughing then and he wasn't laughing now. Here was a bloke who saw the mess I had got myself into and he genuinely cared. We weren't long time friends, we weren't big buddies, it was no skin off his nose which way my life went really, but he was brave enough to leave me in no doubt about the direction I was headed. He didn't give me a lecture, he simply spoke gently and told me I needed help.

Dan finished his drink and drove me up to The Elms where we were to meet Nick. Despite his suggestion in the Four Crosses that I drink no more, I ordered a pint of lager and got him one too. He didn't complain or take me to task over it, he didn't need to. He wasn't my keeper and had no wish to make my decisions for me, he didn't shake his head or ignore me or send me to Coventry, he just smiled limply as he watched me take a sip from the glass. I didn't know it then, but this was to be the last drink I would have to this day. The pub boomed out loud music, young folks in their trendy torn jeans and sloganned t-shirts laughed and giggled around us, strobe lights lit the room. I couldn't hear a word Dan said, nor Nick when he arrived a few minutes later. I stood sullenly, desperate to focus my eyes on something that wasn't moving, yearning now for my bed. Dan and Nick tried to shake me from my trance but I was gone, shot to pieces after ten hours of drinking. They called my friend and housemate, Clem, to come and fetch me.

Clem drove me the five minute journey home, in silence. He didn't know what to say, he felt uncomfortable seeing me this way. I went straight for the kitchen and started preparing beans on toast, ten minutes later Kate arrived. Clem had texted her to say he was collecting me and I was in a state. Kate did the best thing she possibly could have at that moment. She took a look at me, I gave her some self pitying speech about drinking being my choice and no-one had the right to stop me, not that she was suggesting I should, and before it went any further she put her hands in the air and said she was going. Within a minute of her arrival she was gone. This shook me up. I'd been lonely all day, I'd tried to drag friends into drinking with me and they weren't impressed, and now my girlfriend, the woman who I took for granted as being there for me whatever the circumstance, was saying she wasn't going to stick around to be treated this way. I felt marooned. My kids were in Tamworth, my parents were in Scotland, my girlfriend had walked away, my friends were despairing, I was alienating myself fast.

The following morning I awoke to a familiar scene. I'd not drawn the curtains the night before so the sun shone brightly through them, the bedroom light remained on and my clothes were strewn in a heap on the floor apart from those that I'd tumbled into bed still wearing. I opened my eyes, squinted at the sun for a few seconds as I waited to find out what level of hangover it would be today. This usually took about half a minute, a dull, gnawing headache was the norm but if I'd had a particularly long session and forgotten to take onboard a litre of water, it'd be a whole lot worse. As was often the case, a pint glass of water sat untouched on my bedside table. My brain had remembered the routine last night but I'd fallen asleep before drinking the water, and now I was going to suffer. Lying face up, then turning to stare through the window at the trees swaying in the wind, I began to recall the events of yesterday and particularly last night. The upset I'd caused Kate, the worry I'd have caused her parents as she no doubt arrived home tearful, the shame I felt in front of my friends who'd been called upon to rescue me like a lost child. I remembered too the empty feelings I had when sat in those pubs, the realisation that my life as a drinker was not a happy one. For all those bawdy Friday nights out with the lads, there were a dozen soulless, lonely stretches of time where I'd be drinking on my own with only empty cans and music for company. I thought of my job, how long could I continue blagging my way through and holding it down. Where would the money come from to pay for Harry and Hattie if I lost it? I thought about Nurofen, my head was pounding, the worst hangover I could remember and there'd been a few.

I went downstairs, gingerly, every step making my head throb. I drank some water, took some tablets and slumped onto the sofa in front of GMTV. I had work today, an appointment to see a small family business in Birmingham. Under normal circumstances I would certainly have picked up the phone to cancel, but this appointment I had to keep. I was one more customer away from earning a bonus and regardless of how desperate I felt, I simply had to be there. I would have to drive the twelve miles to Birmingham knowing full well that the amount of alcohol resident in my blood stream would comfortably spiral my count above the legal limit for driving, but still I went ahead.

AECC was a business providing drain cleaning services to the public. If you had a blocked drain, you rang your water company, they called out AECC to act on their behalf. It was a family business, ran by husband and wife with a guy named Steve managing the office. I arrived there punctually, the bright sunlight piercing my eyes on a cold, Spring morning as I gobbled another couple of Nurofen, took a large gulp of water and climbed out of my car. I felt like death. My head throbbed to such an extent that I couldn't hold it up, my neck muscles ached and I hung my head low. I was sweating, my body felt like a radiator, and I felt very sick, as if I could throw up at any time.

"Morning Graham," I muttered meekly as he came to the door.

"Alex, good to see you, in you come," smiled Graham, looking sickeningly healthy. "Hey, you alright?" I'd been tumbled already.

"Not really. Have you a glass of water?"

Graham returned with my drink and sat me down in the office with his wife and Steve at their desks alongside. Steve continued his telephone conversation, Gill looked inquisitively at me.

"I think I ate something bad last night. Prawns" I lied. Alcoholics are persistent liars, always a story to cover up their behaviour.

"You should have called, we could have seen you another time."

"No, no. It's best I see you today, I'm away for a week from tomorrow." Another lie. You tell one and they soon come tumbling out. I needed this customer to sign today and I wasn't to be denied.

Graham stood up from his chair, "Look, I've a few things to do, if you want to sit there for fifteen minutes and have a breather, we'll run through those forms after."

Gill returned to her computer and Graham to the yard where he'd been loading the truck up with materials, Steve continued with his telephone conversation. I sat looking at the wall, pining for my bed. This hangover was worse than any other, a migraine type headache had my head feeling like a pressure cooker about to burst, my watery eyes bulged and the perspiration was clinging my shirt to my body. I realised that despite my excuses and lies, these people must be able to smell alcohol as it sweated through my pores. I was reminded of a guy I used to work with who often turned up to work stinking of alcohol, not on his breath, but sweating out of him as a result of the huge intake the night before, I guessed I must smell like him. And if I did, and this customer knew I was lying, which they surely did, I was putting my job on the line being here today. One phone call of complaint and my job was gone, the bank surely frowned upon drunks representing them in front of customers. I was lucky though, these people had grown fond of me during the two meetings we'd held prior and I felt confident they'd not shop me if they had indeed realised I was intoxicated. I couldn't be sure though, my sweating intensified.

Every alcoholic finds the bottom of the barrel at some point and I had found it today. After years of drinking, playing with quitting but not taking it seriously, today I felt a tap on my shoulder. This life I led could not continue any longer, it had become completely unmanageable. I was lonely, I was ashamed, I was putting my job and the security of my children at risk, I was jeopardising relationships. Because of what? Pouring a liquid down my throat. I sat in this draughty office and evaluated the events of yesterday, what had happened for it to get so out of hand? How had I ended up blind drunk in an Aldridge pub on a Monday night with three friends having to organise my journey home? I knew the answer. At 10.30am I had taken a can of Stella from the fridge. It wasn't the eighth can or the fourth pint that did the damage, it was that first drink, without that catalyst, none of this would have happened.

Somehow I negotiated my way through the meeting. Graham and Gill were extremely sympathetic and signed the neccessary forms without fuss or delay, eager for me to return from whence I came. I don't think they did guess that I was hungover, but that's not the point, another day, another customer, and I could have been sussed and out of a job. I cried on the way home, this was surely my lowest ebb, I simply had to do something to arrest this drinking problem that had started at fifteen with a sneaky few sips of Pils, and gained momentum over the years until I found my life utterly unmanageable through drink.

Once home I went straight to bed but the moment I woke up, feeling better but still ill, I reached for my phone book. In there lay the phone number of Peter Messenger, a guy I'd met at a church weekend away the previous Autumn. He'd spoken to me about the counselling work he did with alcoholics, though I hadn't suggested to him that I considered myself to be one, and he'd given me his number for me to keep in touch, "If ever I fancied a chat." He's wise, he knew I had problems despite my denials, and now six months on, I was giving him a call. He met me, we started work together, I've not drank since.

Sound easy? It isn't. You need to put sobriety at the centre of your life, before anything else. You have to remove yourself from temptation which means mixing in different circles, or not mixing at all in certain circumstances. You must eat right, sleep right and exercise. It's a life change, you put it as priority, at the heart of everything you do. And you need support and, most of all, patience from those around you. Thankfully I've been blessed in this department, with Kate's support and God's grace, I've been over three years without a drink and if God never gave me another gift in life, His gift of sobriety is enough to last me a lifetime.

So here I was attempting to become the person Peter had been for me, a counsellor. Seven of us had alighted at a Christian centre in Derby to commence the course, three women in their fifties and three blokes in their thirties. Sheila was the course tutor and administrator who'd pulled all of us together following yards of application forms, laborious registration processes and many phone calls. She'd been planning this for months, finally the induction day had come.

This was the first time I'd been in a classroom, apart from the Speed Awareness course, in eighteen years. It felt surreal, my pens laid out before me next to a spleet new ring binder and a fresh pad of lined paper. I felt like putting my name at the top with the date in the margin, or would Sheila rap me over the knuckles with a ruler for starting without permission. The venue was on a business estate, simple to find as it was right alongside Derby County's football ground which had been heavily signposted since I entered the outskirts of Derby, the sat nav I'd forgotten. It was more of a conference centre really, a huge auditorium with a massive overhead screen accounted for most of the building, but upstairs there were three learning rooms and we were tucked away in the end room, overlooking a river beyond the car park. Tea, coffee and biscuits were laid on, I demolished the biscuits having been in too much of a hurry for breakfast.

I liked the idea of a smaller group. Sheila had suggested from the outset that fifteen people would need to attend to make the course viable but somehow they'd put the course on despite only six being available. I guessed Life For The World had done this to ensure ongoing accreditation and linkage with the University, a course cancellation may have placed this in jeopardy. It suited me, I felt I could work much more effectively with only a handful of students alongside, there'd be more one to one guidance and less reluctance to ask questions, there were fewer people to feel silly in front of. The other students agreed, and as we conversed waiting for Sheila to bring down the hammer and begin, I found out a little about why the others were here. I'd falsely assumed that everyone present would be like me, recovering alcoholics looking to educate themselves so they could work with alcoholics and substance misusers, I was wrong. Sue had paid her own way onto the course believing her work in the Sheffield community would benefit from a knowledge of addictions, James was a chaplain who'd been sponsored to study so he could have an understanding of addictions in young people also to aid him in his work, Lee and Della were already working for organisations that went out to schools to discuss the dangers of drink and drugs, they were interested in obtaining a qualification to further their careers, Susan I didn't speak to you yet. All had valid reasons to be on the course, though none were alcoholics.

The induction day frightened me to death. I'd had no idea what I was getting into but today Sheila spelled it out. Rather naively, I'd been under the dreamy misapprehension that the course would be a fortnightly talking shop where we watched videos then discussed what we'd seen in a cosy group setting before being packed off home with some reading matter. Not a bit of it. This course was on a par with a diploma in terms of course material and we'd be handing in four lengthy assignments by the end of it. The suggested reading list extended to twenty five books and there were equally as many websites recommended from where we could draw information. I panicked. A full-time job, three kids and an already busy life needed to be accommodated around this course and I wasn't sure how I was going to do it. I supposed midnight oil, elbow grease and less golf would be required for starters. But I was committed to this, I wouldn't shy away from the hard work, God had released me from the chains of alcohol and I felt the best way I could serve him was to dedicate myself to this course and thereafter with work in the community, my golf handicap would just have to suffer!

CHAPTER NINETEEN

"… and it's no wonder you can't stand on your own two feet…"

Five games to go, and we needed to win them all to assure ourselves of promotion. Today's game would probably be the toughest of the lot, we were playing the unbeaten league leaders, Rowley College, who had played ten games so far, winning nine and drawing one. Ordinarily this would be a daunting prospect but this league doesn't have any teams so accomplished that they frighten you to death and although they'd had a good run, Rowley were due a defeat.

The weather was favourable, the first true Spring day of the year. Birds singing, sun shining, no hint of rain and just a breath of wind. The pitch was heavy in patches, there'd been torrential rain early in the week, but that apart we were playing in near perfect conditions and at our favoured home ground too. We had no excuses, except perhaps for an injured absentee or two. The first team had an unfamiliar yet familiar look at the back. Defensive stalwarts Joe Lister and Chris Preece weren't able to play due to injury, leaving me and Clem to continue our Keystone Kops act in central defence. Joe's eye was still a concern following its gouging by Matt Brady in training and Chris would have to wear those driving gloves while spectating from the sidelines for another week, he was still struggling with the hamstring strain he'd suffered at St Boniface.

"Should have warmed up properly a couple of weeks back Preece, wouldn't have done your hamstring then," barked Rob Hill.

"Finely tuned athlete me Rob, doesn't take much for a muscle to go," replied Chris.

I reached the groundsman's yard too late to carry the first set of goalposts to the pitch. Instead, four of us carted the second set the extra hundred and odd yards to the other end of the pitch, our hands freezing as we grasped the cold, metal bars. Rich Taylor held on with one hand, making up the numbers while the rest of us bore the weight, this wasn't lost on us and he was given pelters all the way to the six yard box.

When your disciplinary record is as poor as ours, you suddenly notice that the better officials are being asked to referee your games, and linesmen are provided by the league too. It's understandable, your card's been marked and quite rightly the spotlight is upon you, so today we had two black kitted lino's and a ref. On one hand it's flattering, you feel like you really are playing proper amateur football when you have three men in black officiating your game, you've arrived, but on the other it's a little humiliating, an acknowledgement that you're the naughty boys of the league. Either way, the team talk in the dressing room before we trotted out to play, leaned heavily towards discipline and a reminder that we were two or three bookings away from a big fine and possible expulsion. We simply had to keep a lid on our tempers. Late tackles resulting in bookings were part and parcel of the game, everyone understood that, but dissent or bad language was inexcusable. Most of our disciplinary points had been a result of this so we knew where the problems lay, it needed everybody in the team to show some responsibility and self control to prevent jeopardising our position in the league next season.

I'd sneaked a look at the Rowley team photo on the WMCFL website before leaving in the morning. Strange as it may seem, you can sense whether someone's a decent player or not when watching them stand proudly before the camera in their football kit. Sometimes it's a real boost to see these photos declaring a team of virtual teletubbies, grinning all over their faces as they struggle to hold their stomachs in, a sprinkling of lanky geeks thrown in for good measure. You fancy your chances when you see a team like this, clearly in the league just for a laugh and a run around on a Saturday morning. Rowley didn't give this impression though, their team photo suggested rugged defending and impish ball skills. This was gonna be a tough match, I was glad I'd gone running a couple of times in the week because my fitness looked like it would be tested by some of the leaner looking youngsters in the back row.

I felt confident today. There was something about our approach as we huddled together for our team talk before kick off that told me we'd be alright. Often a lacklustre warm up and limp, half hearted grunts of encouragement from seemingly disinterested players tell you the team's not going to be at the races, today though I sensed we were determined. Pig certainly felt the team needed the benefit of his vocal support, I feared for his larynx as the game began with him turning purple, bellowing to his orange shirted team mates from his wide midfield berth. Chris Rodgers wasn't shy in sharing his feelings either and hollered so much in the first half he forgot to play the game, it passed him by entirely. Clem was his usual encouraging self and the handful of spectators and subs cheered us on too, the cacophony of sound was genuinely encouraging, as loud as I'd ever known it.

The wind was knocked out of our sails in the first twenty minutes. Despite enough vocal backing to drown out Birmingham airport, we started tentatively. The ball spent its time in our half with our back four chasing around like startled rabbits as we tried to close down the opposition. My pre-match optimism looked unfounded as we struggled to advance past the halfway line but that said, there were no clearcut chances passed up to Rowley, we succeeded in repelling their attacks once they'd reached the penalty box. A decent away crowd was brought, at least six, something of a record. They were young lads, late teens I'd say, and they were having great sport ridiculing our players one by one. I missed out on the name they labelled me with but there was much hilarity in their ranks when I trotted up to take goal kicks. Our keeper isn't able to kick the ball far and since Preece and Lister were absent, it was my job to take the goal kicks and with me ranging from poor to pathetic in the dead ball department, I made their day. One particularly embarrasing grubber had two of them in stitches, "Where's yer andbag?" one chorused, "I could s*** further than that," shouted another. Typically, we seemed to have more goal kicks today than in any other match I've taken part in and my kicks did improve, but it was rather humiliating seeing the rest of the players push further and further up the pitch and towards me as the match progressed, just waiting for a dolly to fall at their feet.

After half an hour, when we'd decided to take part in the game as an attacking force and not just a defensive one, their number ten reminded me he had a shot on him. Jaimie Hunter his name. I remembered him, he used to play for Kings FC in the First Division but must have decided on a transfer. He was a big bloke, large shoulders, over six foot and of sturdy build, carrying a bit too much timber but using his strength wisely, laying the ball off for others to do the running. After a brief spell of St Thomas pressure, we found ourselves defending again as the ball was lobbed into Hunter's chest. He controlled the ball expertly, spun around and lashed it towards goal from a distance of twenty five yards. After three yards of its journey, my face intercepted, the ball crashing into my hooter and pole axing me. I sat on the turf dumbfounded, I felt like a cartoon character who'd just been clonked over the head by a hammer, stars were circling over my head while little birdies tweeted. Jaimie Hunter found this funny, so did everyone else, there's nothing funnier than seeing someone taking a full tilt volley full in the face or gonads. He offered his hand to pull me up, his merry band of supporters hooting their joy at my expense, I was definitely becoming their hapless figure of fun today, they'd snigger about me in the pub tonight and no mistake. But like the pro' I am, I shrugged my shoulders and got on with the game, I'd taken one for the team and now I had a job to do. What a hero.

Hunter proved more than irksome in another area too. His throw ins were enormous, Rowley's every throw from inside our half launched into the penalty area like a corner kick. We had countless aerial bombardments aimed at our six yard box and Rob in goal made great work of them if defenders didn't make the header. But despite these constant assaults from the skies, it was a long throw of our own which saw the game's opening goal, an embarrassing one as far as their keeper was concerned. Our right back Andy Carter hurled the ball into the box, it bounced once and reached the keeper who flapped at it like a seal clapping it's fins, clawing it apologetically into the net. The poor chap was crestfallen, we were elated. We'd not had a shot worthy of the name in the whole of the first half yet had somehow managed to take the lead.

Half-time. Not for us a walk to a cosy dressing room for a rub down and change of shirt. No ball boys handing out plastic bottles of high energy drinks as we left the pitch, no sign of a concertinaed tunnel being extended to make a gangway to enter the changing room area. No, half-time for us is a stagger across to our kit bags lying at the side of the pitch in case they're nicked from the changing rooms, to find a bottle of water if we'd remembered it. There's no silence in court while the manager gives us the hair dryer treatment, we tend to split into twos and threes to exchange opinions on why everything we as individuals are doing is right and everything everyone else is doing is wrong. If you spot someone amongst the handful of spectators who you recognise, you'll go over and chew the fat for a minute or two, but after a couple of minutes everyone's raring to go again and you trot back for the second half. There's no fanfare, just a silent trudge back to your mark with your legs telling you they've had enough. I walked past a piece of dog dirt around the left back position and decided that since I may be patrolling that area in the second half, it'd be an idea to kick it off the pitch. This I tried but soon found it wasn't hard enough to be kicked, it simply smeared itself across the toe of my boot, I stubbed it into the turf and carried on regardless. You don't get trouble like that at Old Trafford.

The second half mirrored the first, all out attack from Rowley with very little attacking from us. It was backs to the wall all the way and the game became rather more feisty, late tackles and verbals taking over for a minute or two until, despite all of the pleading before the game about retaining our discipline, we received a booking. And who was this hoodlum unable to keep control of his temper after a minor dust up with the opposition? None other than Richard Taylor, part-time midfielder, full time man of the cloth, on the end of a yellow card at a time when his church team were staring expulsion in the face. Marvellous. He'd gone into a fifty-fifty tackle, both players going to ground, and when getting to their feet, the Rowley player had pushed his nose towards Rich's in an act of provocation, to be fair to the Minister, his reaction was to stand firm, not to antagonise but to smile at the player and diffuse the situation. The Rowley player was having none of it though and the nose to nose set to continued for a couple of seconds until the referee scurried over, and in an attitude of 'six of one, half a dozen of the other' decided he'd book them both for unsporting behaviour. Absolutely crackers. It got worse minutes later when Podge was also booked, supposedly for throwing the ball away but in fact he'd thrown it to the precise point where the free-kick was to be taken, but hadn't done so in a manner to the referee's liking, he'd walked away with the ball and returned it high over his head as he ambled towards his own goal. Two ridiculous bookings, we were now only one away from oblivion.

The siege continued, Rowley occupying our half of the pitch with wave after wave of attack, my legs were going to pack in if the ref didn't blow soon but there was still ten minutes to go. Finally, our defence was breached, but in controversial circumstances. A right wing cross evaded onrushing attackers and back pedalling defenders until finding their winger ghosting in at the back post to arrow a low shot from eight yards. Rob scrambled across to prevent the goal, sliding feet first rather than diving onto it with his hands, which there was no time to do. He clattered the ball away with the opposition jumping in the air, arms aloft, claiming it had crossed the line. The ref looked up to his linesman who lifted the flag of doom to confirm it had indeed rolled over the line. 1-1. St Thomas players and supporters were united in their disgust at the decision, 'Never a goal' they cried, but as the deepest defender with a bird's eye view of proceedings, I confirmed to them afterwards that it was a legitimate goal, the giveaway surely being the fact that Rob's studs got tangled in the back of the net when he tried to clear the ball.

The game finished one each, a fair result but a disappointing one as far as our promotion push was concerned. In truth, if anyone deserved to win it was Rowley, we'd ridden our luck and created precious few chances, Mark Hadden for once failing to make the scoresheet. We learned later that the teams around us had picked up points too so our bid for promotion was now out of our hands, even if we won our remaining games we needed others to slip up. Still, we'd played a good team today who'd shown us why they'd been league leaders, and when the referee's booking your vicar who hasn't got a bone of aggressive intent in his body, you know you're on to a loser.

	Played	Points
City Church	13	30
Rowley College	11	29
Dynamo Kingswinford	13	28
Us	14	26
Zion Athletic	14	23
Halesowen Zion	12	21

CHAPTER TWENTY

"... I don't need an attitude, rebellion is a platitude..."

Four games left, or should that be three and a formality, since today we were at home to the league's perennial whipping boys, Brierley Hill. A nicer bunch of guys you couldn't wish to meet but they were truly hapless. For every goal they scored they conceded six, a record they'd 'boasted' for years now. Some teams you take great delight in beating, rubbing their noses in defeat after they'd posed and preened their way through ninety minutes, but you felt guilty each time you thrashed Brierley Hill, which we had done twice already this season, 5-1 and 8-1. They never had a cross word with the ref and played every match with a tremendous spirit, they were by far the nicest team in the league. They took their beatings with good grace, always a friendly handshake at the final whistle to congratulate you on having taken them to the cleaners. We'd beat them today while smoking a pipe and wearing carpet slippers.

Not only were we playing a traditionally dire team, but we were playing them on the back of our eight match unbeaten run. That said, the midweek Championship fixtures had given me the willies, seven of the eight clubs chasing promotion to the Premiership either lost or drew matches they were expected to win with something to spare. This could happen to us if we didn't have the right attitude.

Well, we had our minds on the game alright, so much so that we were paralysed with self imposed hype and suffocated by a do or die attitude. We forgot we were playing football and went solemnly into battle as if it were the most serious event of our adult lives. Fully kitted up forty minutes before kick-off, we sprinted out in unison to stretch and warm up before hammering back to the changing rooms for a five minute team talk that Winston Churchill would have been proud of. And while we were treating the game as if our lives depended on it, Brierley Hill sauntered along to our place without a care in the world, arriving fifteen minutes before kick-off and drifting onto the pitch just in time for the ref's starting pistol. They didn't have enough kit to go round so one player wore an Inter Milan home shirt and another a black

polo neck zip up top which did nothing for him as it clung
unflatteringly to his jelly belly. They looked unprepared, unfit and ready
for a return to bed, football appeared to be the last thing on their minds
while we stood like angry bulls, pawing the turf with our hooves, steam
blowing out of our nostrils.

We were so psyched up that we'd managed to talk all of the joy out
of the occasion. I sensed that if we'd been offered the three points
without playing we'd have taken them. Was that a football pitch before
us or the World War II trenches? Veins popping, eyes bulging, we'd
have strangled our own grandmothers for three points. It was crackers.
Not a smiling face amongst us as we took our positions for the start,
defenders barking orders at midfielders, midfielders demanding
unswerving commitment from strikers, our opposition looking at us
wondering if we'd bet our mortgages on the outcome of this game. Even
the referee looked frightened.

I can't bring myself to give you a blow by blow account of the game
but suffice to say we lost, contriving a two-one reverse despite
dominating possession for ninety minutes. We played on our home
pitch, on a sunny day, against third from bottom opposition, and we
blew it. Not only did we blow it but the manner in which we blew it
made it all the more disappointing; berating each other for errors of any
kind, slagging off the referee, giving our own linesman pelters for
having the honesty to flag us for offside, earning yet another booking for
senseless dissent, but most frustrating of all, we disappeared as a
cohesive team unit and over the course of ninety minutes capitulated
into a team of individuals looking for someone else to blame. And all
because we'd forgotten what we were there for, to have a game of footie
amongst friends. We'd put so much pressure on ourselves that we felt
too uptight to play, straight jacketed into a game thanks to fear. I was
one of the worst culprits, perpetually haranguing the referee and
moaning at the midfield for not holding the ball up, I become a right
arse sometimes when I'm on a football pitch. In my case, the poor
behaviour and attitude was borne out of frustration with my own
ineptitude, I had a bad game and so turned to others to blame. Powder
puff heading and pansy potter tackling left my team mates in trouble

time after time, and the young centre forward I found myself marking left me scrambling around in the mud twice in each half, bolting away with the ball both times. It doesn't do much for an old man's dignity, chasing a youngster around like that, marking him was like trying to spoon up the elusive last cornflake as it floats around in the milk of your cereal bowl, so like an idiot I scythed him down and risked a yellow card instead, senseless considering our disciplinary record.

I can rightly claim to have been at fault for both goals, marking fresh air when a cross came in for their striker to bury a header, and being had up like a kipper by their young number nine who left me for dead for their second, laying on a pass for his partner in crime to notch the winner. In between Mark Hadden had scored an equaliser for us. In ninety minutes of football I produced only one worthwhile contribution: chasing back to clear the ball off the line only because my own sliced clearance had sailed over the head of our bemused keeper. After this abject performance I wondered whether I'd done the right thing returning to football after considering retirement post St Mary's. I loved playing football, and didn't overlook the positive impact it had on my life in terms of fitness both physical and mental, but when you're being shown up for the ageing duffer you are by a kid half your age it's more than a little humiliating. Or had I just had the stinker all players get from time to time and the last three games of the season would revive my confidence and interest in next season? We'd see. Either way, St Thomas would be playing Second Division football next season with or without me, the promotion party could now be cancelled in favour of a wake. We'd lost, and in terms of our promotion push, today had been a disaster on the scale of your mother ironing creases down your jeans.

Emily awoke on Monday morning at her usual hour of 5.30am. She'd had another restless night, demanding attention from her Mum at silly o'clock and now deciding to start her day before the rest of the world awoke. Still, I'm an early riser and don't mind taking on the first shift of the day, although 5.30am is a little on the rude side, another hour and I might feel less hard done by. The clocks were to go forward in a week's time, I hoped Emily's body clock would pay attention to this.

I brought her downstairs, plonked her in her bouncy chair and turned on the morning news. Knife crime dominated Natasha Kaplinsky's attention, why was it people found it necessary to plunge knives into each other? What was it about the human psyche that had us resorting to carrying knives around to begin with? I'm far from qualified to judge such matters and it was too early in the day to consider my opinion for long, so I turned over to trusty old Sky Sports where I could watch highlights of last night's match. Global warming and youth crime may have been the major topics of the day, but this day hadn't really started yet as far as I was concerned, I'd plead ignorance for a while longer and watch a re-run of Colchester v Derby instead.

Another day another dollar, but sometimes I wondered whether my working day served any purpose at all and whether I genuinely earned my money. Friday had found me touring Birmingham to no obvious effect; a visit to a meat wholesaler who'd forgotten I was coming and didn't show up, a meeting with a complainant, who I'd signed up six months prior, in order for him to accuse me of mis-selling, and an aborted meeting with a printer whom I realised within fifteen minutes of arrival that we could do nothing for. I returned home in a bit of a daze, I might as well have stayed with Emily or mown the lawn. Good days and bad days. There'd been plenty of good lately, but days like this left you wondering why you left your scratcher in the morning.

Children have a wonderful ability of bringing you down to earth though, reminding you what life is truly about; love for one another. I get so hung up with my insular working world sometimes that I forget to smell the flowers, Emily, Harry and Hattie return me to my senses and I thank God for them. They're different personalities, but each has the gift of making their father smile, take a deep breath and appreciate that work is very much secondary in life. Harry with his cheek, Hattie with her humour and Emily with her babbling. I'm something of an intrigue to each of them, they never know what I'm going to do next, neither do I. Life is never dull when they've a mad Dad around, I have many inhibitions in adult company but seemingly none at all when my kids are with me, I become a child myself. I reckon my absence from Harry and Hattie's day to day life has contributed to this, were we to live together

I'd probably not be the extrovert I appear to be to them, but since we have limited time together, I wonder if I subconsciously act up a little. The true test will be how my relationship develops with Emily, she has me around every day of her life, so if she's embarrassed to be with me by the time she's ten then I'll know who the real me truly is.

But marvelling at your children and letting your mind disappear into a fluffy world of family harmony does not pay the mortgage. I had another day's work to look forward to, this time in the company of a bank manager as we visited the premises of Chief Printing where a gallery of directors lay in wait. Nine times out of ten I deal with owners of small businesses, one to one meetings over a cup of coffee in a relaxed, informal atmosphere. They love their businesses, it's their life, and they're only too happy to tell you all about where they came from, how they started and what a success they've been. I simply ask them to tell me a little about their company and off they go, a This Is Your Life style history from birth of the business to present day, they love it. And I love hearing about it, every story is different and very often incorporates an account of their personal life along the way -

"Yeah, me and the missus, well, we weren't really seein eye to eye so I sez, 'Look woman, if I don't run this business we don't have a house, it pays the bills or didn't yer know?' Well, of course she left me then for a younger model, think she'd met him at the gym, but that's by the by, where were we? Oh yeah, that's right, invoice financing..."

The companies I visit have very few workers, more often than not just the owner and a couple of part time office staff, and it's a very down to earth, free and easy meeting. I listen to them, they listen to me, there's no ulterior agenda, we simply discuss whether the product I present is suitable for their business and we come to an agreement one way or another. Larger businesses on the other hand, such as Chief Printing who I was visiting today, were a different proposition altogether and I found meetings with them extremely awkward. Rather than a friendly handshake with a humble owner, you'd find yourself seated in a magazine strewn waiting room with a fern plant for company, before being marched upstairs by a haughty secretary, like a lamb being led to the slaughter, into a boardroom to be faced by a row of stern looking directors ready for the kill. I'm generalising now but nine times out of ten, the reception would be decidedly frosty, proper businessmen lying in wait for the bank, suspicious that we were planning to turn them over. They'd rarely let you into their world, no warmth just business speak, a few niceties but no chance of rapport building, it'd be straight down to financial matters in hand. There were exceptions, some folk's back room businesses had multiplied in size, the success of their company catching them by surprise, and they sat awkwardly in their semi-plush offices costing them a couple of quid but not too much, there may be a rainy day around the corner. They hadn't intended to be several million pound turnover organisations, it just seemed to spiral as they went quietly about their way, unawares. These people still had their feet on the ground, they merely had photos of fast sports cars on their office walls while the Chief Printing directors of this world drove them. And they still wore open necked shirts and sweaters, not pin striped stiff collared shirts with cufflinks. You can always spot a director of a medium to large business, or a bank salesmen in the medium to large sector for that matter, they wear cufflinks while the rest of us mere mortals are happy to button our sleeves down.

Richard, the company's bank manager, and I were wheeled in to battle. We were introduced to four company directors and their accountant who fixed us with a steely glare as if to say, 'You ain't gonna put anything past these guys without my say so.' Tea, water and biscuits were brought through on a tray as Richard attempted to break the ice with some talk on the weekend's football. "We were at Twickenham," bragged one of them, "watching the French take a caning. Shame for them isn't it?" he guffawed as his fellow directors sniggered dutifully. He'd be the boss then. I could picture him rolling up to Twickers in his 4x4, throwing open the hatchback and sharing a flask and sandwiches with his rugger mates from a tartan rug, swapping patronising stories about 'the wife' and exchanging snippets about their last game of golf. These men often seemed to have regulation toilet seat hair arrangements or spectacular comb overs, perhaps their bravado was a result of a subconscious inferiority complex due to hair loss. Or maybe I read too much into things. Regardless, while they were mincing about at the rugger, I was making fuzzy felt characters at home with Hattie, a much more preferable option to my mind than playing Hurrah Henrys for an afternoon.

The meeting was returned to business matters after the Managing Director finished telling us of his planned fishing trip to Pitlochry where, naturally, a friend owned a piece of land. He would fly there and back in a day don't you know.

"So nice of you gentleman to see us today, now, what are you going to do about these exhorbitant prices you've been quoting us?"

Richard and I exchanged glances and waited for each other to pick up the baton. The silence went on rather too long and our customers could surely sense they had the upper hand already with us squirming in our seats, so I dived in before it went on any longer.

"What aspect of the pricing do you feel is expensive?" I ventured.

Mr Setter, the financial boffin within the business, peered over the rim of his spectacles and said curtly, "All of it". Entirely predictable though his reply was, it was received with another obedient guffaw by his fellow directors. I allowed him his moment but left the silence in the air deliberately this time, he'd need to substantiate his claim once the applause had subsided.

"Well for starters, the set up fee, how can you justify that? Banks love to throw in a set up fee but from where I'm sitting there's nothing to it and it certainly doesn't warrant a thousand pounds. Plus VAT I assume?" He whined.

"Yes it does include VAT," I replied, "and while I may be the face of the bank before you today, and not necessarily a pretty one I accept, there is a lot of work done in the background by many people to enable this facility to be set up for you."

"So we pay you to set up an arrangement which you'll charge us even more for using?" replied a smug Mr Setter, leaning back in his chair, removing his glasses and placing them in his suit's breast pocket. He looked like Siegfried Farnon, off All Creatures Great & Small, after he'd castigated his younger brother Tristan. He was certainly behaving like an actor, revelling in his role before an attentive audience of co-directors, ambushing their bank manager into dropping his prices. They could try it with Richard sat alongside me, but I wasn't buckling. I bristle when I deal with people like this, they may be clever and they may be succesful businessmen, but no amount of arrogance is going to make me compromise my position when it comes to set up fees.

"Well I've come here today, with Richard, to help outline the various options available to your business in terms of moving your business forward," (oh yes, I can do business speak too you know) all come at a cost I'm afraid, but I think you'll find that each is aimed at benefitting the business. I won't try and persuade you one way or another, but I won't pretend we can make savings for you in terms of the set up fee."

I looked at each of the four directors, aware that I'd been sharp and unequivocal but hoping they'd received this approach with a grudging respect rather than thinking I had a bare faced cheek not being prepared to drop the price. Richard was wincing a little, I think he'd hoped for a bit more movement from me. When it comes to pricing I believe you've to stick to your guns and maintain credibility, the moment you start dropping your trousers there's no telling how far you'll have to go.

Returning his glasses to his eyes and sitting forward again, Mr Setters looked down at my written quotation. I'd won this battle but he wasn't finished with the war.

"And your service charge, 0.4% of turnover. By my calculations that equates to around fifteen thousands pounds a year, have I miscalculated or is that correct?"

I fished my calculator out of my pocket and began to crunch the figures. I knew the answer but wanted to buy a bit of time before I answered, another immediate, stark response from me might upset them and make me look intransigent.

"Can you remind me what turnover your business is projecting over the next twelve months?" I enquired, again fully aware of the answer but wanting to look as if there was thought going into the pricing of the deal for them and not simply a blanket figure.

"Three million," came the response from Tony Spiers, MD, after a conflab between the four of them.

"There may be some movement on our pricing there then," I

encouraged them, "Depending on the length of contract you're looking for." Their eyes lit up as the prospect of saving money reared its head, two of them sat forward and one crossed his legs, a sign to me that they were interested in a deal but wanted to nail the cost element of it here and now. I would be happy to oblige.

"On average customers remain with us for over four years. With that in mind, if you sign a contract for three years rather than the two years for which I've previously quoted, we can reduce the pricing." I threw this out to ascertain interest and wasn't surprised to hear the response, "By how much?"

This really was a quickfire meeting. Within five minutes of Mr Spiers trout and whisky plans being unveiled to a disinterested Richard and myself, we were dealing with the nitty gritty of striking a deal. Buying signals can be hard to spot sometimes, but these guys were carrying I MUST SIGN NOW placards around the boardroom and bellowing, "Sign me up, sign me up!" through a corporate loud hailer. Get this pricing right and I'd be back within a week to sign up a lucrative deal.

As any self respecting salesman would do, I'd built a bit of room into my initial offer of 0.4% and whether they wanted a two or three year deal, there was plenty of leeway. I stoically lifted the lid of my laptop and entered my password, explaining to the room that it'd take a few seconds before I could reach my pricing model. As was the intention, this bought me more time, Richard engaging them with other banking matters as my grey cells toiled, what price did I think I could get away with without losing the deal? Other banks were surely quoting and if I got too cute I'd lose the customer to the competition. I wondered who else they'd spoken to? Big name, high street banks? In which case the pricing would be tight. Smaller, independent providers? In which case I barely needed to tickle the pricing to win the business. How could I find out?

The company's accountant had remained silent during the meeting and I had a strong feeling that he would have a major say in which way the company would go. You find this with accountants, their opinion is trusted by customers and rightly so, since it's their job to provide not only accounting services but also suggest methods in which the company can save costs. He'd suggested to them that invoice discounting was the best way forward and the directors were in agreement, it was just a case of securing the best deal. Many accountants have tie-ins with invoice financing providers and are paid healthy commissions for business introduced, I'd be interested to determine whether Mr Dalton, sat quietly in his dark suit and looking on with intent, was the sort of accountant who enjoyed such a relationship. I needed to do some fishing of my own.

" Mr Dalton, does your practice operate the SAGE accounting package?" Almost certainly 'yes' would be the answer.

"Yes we do," he obliged, seemingly chuffed that I'd asked a question of him and his company.

"And I take it you use broadband?"

"Oh yes, we have many computers and all are networked and linked to broadband. It allows us to work much more efficiently and respond to our clients needs quickly" he pined. Okay, okay, I didn't need a sales pitch from him. That was my job.

"We have an online system which enables customers to use our facility electronically, I don't know if you deal with other invoice discounting companies but not all have the ability to communicate electronically," I suggested.

"Well, yes we do deal with an invoice discounting house for one of our other clients but I have to say the system which you describe is not something currently that we benefit from. Everything is dealt with via the post."

Bingo. It was an independent provider he used, their pricing would be through the roof compared to ours. I didn't need to lop off much from my pricing at all. Happy days indeed.

The meeting sauntered to a finish, the pricing issue soon resolved when I dropped our charges just enough to make it look worthwhile to the company while still making it worth the banks while too. That's the point of a customer/supplier relationship surely, something in it for both parties. Mr Setters threw a couple of curve balls at me in an attempt to trip me up, stuff about the administrative nature of our relationship appearing onerous, but a flourish of my laptop's demonstration and a few soothing words later, he was content enough. Richard had been given a harder time than me, having to offer free bank charges, guaranteed regular contact and the shirt off his back if I remember rightly. We all shook hands to conclude the meeting and parted on the understanding that there was a deal to be done if we could call them to book a sign up over the following few days.

I returned to my car, loosened my tie and collected my voicemail messages. "You have nine new messages," the recorded voice warbled. Oh what it was to be so important. I listened to them one by one until reaching the most vital. "Hello Alex, it's Rob. The game's been moved to the mornin' on Saturday, hope you can play." Brilliant. I had a match to look forward to at the weekend.

CHAPTER TWENTY ONE

"… it's me for you and you for me…"

With the promotion challenge all over bar the shouting, St Thomas assembled their weary carcasses at The Stick & Wicket for the final home match of the season. The groundsman likes to protect his precious turf ahead of the cricket season, so by the end of March football is strictly forbidden, to give him time to convert the pitch into a cricket field. Bunch of namby pamby cricketers, needing their grass just so, frightened they might get mud on their gleaming white flannels. Big jessies, you don't see footballers wearing pads, boxes and helmets. Or pyjamas.

So this was to be our last outing on home soil, and pretty poignant it was too. Twelve months ago, a young lad was turning out regularly for our club, Oliver Hewitt his name. Tragically, he died in his sleep one evening having suffered only flu symptoms as he went to bed, a man I never met, but having learned about him from those who did, I wish I had. His sister and grandfather marked the anniversary by attending our fixture, it was a humbling experience meeting them, they were at the very centre of our thoughts as Rob Hill brought along flowers, possibly the largest bouquet seen in public since Dame Edna last appeared on stage, and Joe Lister presented them to Ollie's sister. Both teams stood around the centre circle for a minute's silence, after a prayer dedicated to Ollie and his family. We marked the moments respectfully and talked before the game about the tragedy of Ollie's death and how desperately he'd have wanted to be involved in a game, any game, of football. We wanted to do his memory justice, not with a win, but with an attitude.

Daz Smail came up with an ingenious game plan as we sat around chatting in the dressing room, drawing instant agreement all around him. It was a revolutionary idea that we were only sorry it had taken a full season to discover; how about we go out and enjoy it? Why not put the rabble rousing team talk aside for a day, along with the belligerent, growling win at all costs attitude, and try to enjoy a game of football?

It was what we needed to hear, permission to play without fear or panic, to have fun, to play footie with our mates and not batten down the hatches for an all out war. Today's game wasn't to be a re-enactment of the Charge Of The Light Brigade, though we'd probably be trounced in a similar fashion, nor was it a scrap with a neighbouring school, it was eleven blokes pretending to be kids again, having a kick around with eleven like minded individuals. So it was agreed, no pressure, no grim, po-faced determination, just a relaxed game of football on a sunny Spring morning. We were determined to win, but we were going to set about it in a fashion that didn't ruin the occasion.

Our squad was reduced to twelve with the unavailability of Buzz (in Rome), Preecey (still crocked), Brady (holidaying somewhere or other) and Chris Rogers (whereabouts unknown). For the final time Ian Pearsall would have to sit the game out due to the suspension he'd suffered following his earlier indiscretions. To his great credit he'd not disappeared from view while serving his five week ban but attended every game, encouraging from the sidelines, making peace with officials he'd offended and remaining very much part of the scene. I admired him greatly. It'd have been easy for him to sulk, to disappear, to feel the world was against him and take his bat home, instead he took his punishment standing up straight. It reminded me of the time I upset the school bully at Mackie Academy all those years ago. "Take your hiding Russon," Fergy used to bellow before laying into me with punches that we both felt were fully justified, I'd taken my hiding then and Ian was accepting his now, showing just how much being part of the club meant to him. I couldn't wait for him to come back, there were still two games left this season for him to make his mark, hopefully for the right reasons this time.

Although our promotion plans had gone for a burton with last week's shocking home defeat, our opponents today, Halesowen Zion, still harboured realistic hopes of a move up to Division One. They were lying just three points from the team in third place and started the game in the same manner that we had the previous week, screaming at each other like demented hyenas in an effort to encourage but merely spreading panic throughout the side and motivating their opponents instead. It's a peculiarity of sport that if you've nothing to play for but know you can scupper your opponents push for promotion, your workrate doubles. Knowing how much the game meant to them acted as our incentive, perhaps this is a little spiteful but that's football, the team sitting third in the league certainly wouldn't have wanted us to roll over and neither would we had the roles been reversed.

Determination was a must if I was to get through this game with a modicum of pride still intact, pitted again as I was against a young whipper snapper of a striker, twinkle toed and with blinding pace. This was a mismatch of Tyson v Danny LaRue proportions. He was half my age, twice my ability and if I didn't get my act together the gulf in class was going to shine like a Belisha beacon across the streets of Aldridge. It didn't get off to a good start. He 'megged me in the first ten minutes before delivering an inch perfect cross that their centre forward spooned over the bar. He ghosted past me the following minute, leaving me to eat dirt while he spanked a long range shot narrowly wide and not long after, my humiliation was complete when an attempted slide tackle saw me disappear off the pitch while he dragged the ball back and stood still with it at his feet. I was relieved he didn't give it the old 'ship ahoy' trick, looking into the distance beneath a right hand shading his eyes. Mercifully, probably out of sympathy for the old man at the back, their manager switched my nemesis across to the other side of the forward line within twenty minutes and I was spared further embarrassment. To my great relief, I'd instead be marking the rotund Lee Ralph, tidy player but akin to a tugboat when turning, by the time he span around you'd had ample time to clear your lines. I'd need to concentrate but at least it was an even contest now, Clem would have to scamper after Speedy Gonzalez instead.

We battled hard but looked second best from the off and Halesowen's superiority was confirmed when they scored following a deep cross to an unchallenged striker. The back four looked at each other for someone to blame, the midfield helped us out in this regard by identifying all four of us as being culpable, ahh teamwork. If only someone could explain to midfielders across the land that they have defensive responsibilities too, midfield isn't only about badly timed forward surges and misplaced passes, neither is it about lazy hoofs into the corners for hapless strikers to plod after, or hiding from the ball when throw-in takers are looking for a team-mate. Further, effective midfield play is not about ducking 50/50's or driving free-kicks into defensive walls, continuing petty squabbles with an opposing midfielder who's outclassed you or blaming the surface when you slice a raking pass out of play that by rights, you should be proferring a written apology to the manager for. You think us defenders don't notice these things eh? Well we do.

We dusted ourselves down after conceding the opening goal and readied ourselves for the restart. Tempers remained under control and the berating of team mates was conspicious by its absence for once, as was the haranguing of the referee. True to our word, we were going to enjoy today and not shoot ourselves in the foot with fear. Tony Walker typified this attitude from his position at right back, strolling around nonchalantly as if walking his dog in the park, fiddling with the ball in his own six yard box when it needed wailing out of the ground. He never batters the ball away Tony, he'd rather muck about with it even if he is standing in the most dangerous area of the pitch with opponents crowding in on him. If the scores were level in the ninetieth minute of a cup final and you were trying to clear a corner, Walker's feet is the last place you'd want the ball to be. He'd already gifted them a golden chance with a scuffed pass across the eighteen yard box landing at their striker's feet, the shocked striker dollying his shot into Rob's midriff so taken aback was he at the gift horse landing before him. One day Mr Walker will learn that you can't win a game of football in your own eighteen yard box but you can certainly lose one (copyright Alan Hansen).

My goal kick hell continued for another week despite me pleading with my fellow defenders to take their turn. All were reluctant, possibly because I'd be denying them their weekly cheer, more likely because they could no more get the ball off the ground than I could. The results were better this week, but still I heard the familiar cry from their captain, "Close in lads, it 'aye gooin' far". In my defence, my only effort to clear the halfway line, a gust of wind carrying it through, set up a mazy run from Matt Challoner who won a corner kick. I lumbered forward to make a nuisance of myself in the box and was promptly presented with the best chance of the game, Nick Jones' corner arriving at knee height for me to lash home with my left foot. My intentions were honourable as I drew my foot back, but I inevitably muffed the opportunity to score, missing the ball completely as my limp left leg dangled itself out to dry. Cue hilarity all round.

We had a couple more opportunities in the second half but didn't trouble the keeper and as the game petered out, it looked for all the world like Halesowen Zion would be celebrating a 1-0 victory. We were taking our pending defeat like men this time, with honour, keeping our discipline and not reducing ourselves to the in-fighting of last week until miraculously, with three minutes remaining, another Nick Jones corner was curled in this time for their right back to inexplicably nod into his own net. Get in! We'd sneaked a draw. We were cock-a-hoop, the righteous had indeed been smiled upon, we'd set about the game with a refreshing attitude, fought hard despite being on the receiving end of something of a battering, and notched a late equaliser which we very much deserved. We'd even drawn a blank on the yellow card front while Halesowen had the ref scribbling in his notebook twice.

Promotion was out of the question for us, it had been before the game, but it was now almost impossible for Halesowen Zion too, we'd meet them again next season. Perversely perhaps, we left the field feeling happier than we had a few weeks prior having beaten St Boniface. Football that day had nothing to do with enjoyment, we'd lost track of what we were playing the game for, we'd been determined but steely eyed, morose and business-like with it, the three points being a relief not a joy. Today however we'd turned the tables and reminded ourselves, thanks to Daz's pre-match talk, that we were here to enjoy a game of footie before returning home to our friends and families, we were not going into battle at Dunkirk. We'd been rewarded for our approach, we were happy with our draw, and it had been an honour to represent St Thomas again, especially on this of all days, the anniversary of Ollie's passing.

CHAPTER TWENTY TWO

"… trying to be someone I know I'm not…"

I'm quite good at my job. It's not what I left school aiming for, and describing myself as a Business Development Manager at parties doesn't command instant respect, but I'm happy in my work.

There's a three tier system of hierarchy within the sales team at the bank, a three rung ladder with me firmly entrenched on rung one. I sell finance to small businesses, the guys on rung two sell to medium sized businesses, and rung three-ers deal with companies turning over squillions of pounds. Bigger companies with even bigger egos. I'm content though to deal with life's smaller fish, down to earth company owners, people who will shake hands on a deal with me provided I talk straight. They don't appreciate waffle from a slimy rep, they want the bottom line and I give it. When I show up for a meeting, the guy greeting me may be aboard a forklift truck, the company owner, and we'll conduct exploratory discussion shouting above the screech of a nearby bandsaw, as he shifts packs of timber around the yard. It's earthy and feels real, way preferable to negotiating, as rung two-ers do, with career minded, arrogant posers staring down their noses across a cheap desk in their Habitat inspired offices, trying to prove their worth by saving a quid off already generous prices. If I was to gain promotion I'd have to deal with people like that every day of the week and I didn't fancy it, so happily stayed put on rung one, until…

… money talked and the offer of a further few grand on my basic salary persuaded me to reassess. My boss had been massaging my ego for a while, appealing to the dollar signs that flashed before every salesman's eyes. The company, he explained, were 'benchmarking' for potential vacancies on rung two and though there were no jobs available currently, clearing the initial hurdle of the assessment would mean I'd be through to a 'chat with the boss' type interview when a job did come up, apparently imminently. I agreed to take part, particularly when my boss intimated the assessment would be a mere rubber stamping exercise conducted by two colleagues he knew very well, both of whom apparently wanted me in the job. Unless I threw scalding water over them or denigrated their grandparents, I was destined to succeed, and within a few weeks it was expected I'd be five grand a year richer and driving a classy motor.

We met in the company's palatial Birmingham office, all oak desks, doctor's surgery table lamps and two inch deep shag pile carpet. Although feeling justifiably complacent about my chances, I'd donned my best suit (i.e. the newer of the two I owned) and cleaned my shoes, (with a damp dishcloth), eager to convey the right impression. The two fellows orchestrating the assessment day, Bob and Norman, had also decided the occasion warranted smarter than normal attire, both looking resplendent in white collared shirts and dark suits. The offices normally contained casually clothed employees since they weren't customer facing, so job interviews were a dead giveaway to everybody, you were wearing a tie in the office all of a sudden and stood out like a sore thumb.

I was greeted at the door by Bob and Norman, their manner towards me unusual from the start, with Bob thanking me for coming and Norman offering to fetch me a coffee. Both seemed officious, even respectful, not something they could normally be accused of and I'd known them for four years. We bantered tamely but they kept their distance, persevering with a new found penchant for officialdom by inviting me to sign the visitors book. No-one signed the visitors book, but today somehow it was deemed necessary, so here, within sixty seconds of arrival, my mood had already managed to journey from 'composed' to 'uncomfortable', and I'd barely said hello.

The atmosphere of unease continued into the boardroom with Norman encouraging banal conversation. I agreed Chelsea were looking good for the title again this season and yes, the weather was good for the time of year, before being invited to sit down. Norman chose to stand from his position opposite, towering over his subject, reading out the agenda as if it were the case for the prosecution.

"Structured interview first," he said, "then a break for lunch with a role play to follow. Do you have any special dietary needs?"

"Pie and chips would be good," I grinned, a lame attempt to inject some ice breaking humour to proceedings but Norman was having none of it. Neither was Bob. They looked at me before taking their seats.

The structured interview began. The three of us sitting in the boardroom, perched at one end of a veneered, sandy, brown table upon which rested a large jug of water, a sprinkling of plastic cups, three notepads and three pencils. Bob and Norman sat side by side, continuing to smile weakly before Norman opened with question number one.

"Can you give us an example of how your tenacity has won the company business that may otherwise have been lost?"

I heaved an inward sigh of despair. The circus had begun. A crock of a question to be greeted with a crock of an answer, signalling the onset of an hour or more of unashamed self promotion with diplomacy and internal politics all to be factored in. I was to imply naked ambition and the willingness to selflessly hoover up all potential customers in the Midlands area for the good of the bank. I'd expected an opener along these lines, and it allowed me the opportunity to fish a pat answer out of my back pocket, dripping with smug, self satisfaction, and encouraging the shameless blowing of one's own trumpet. I wanted to say simply that people buy people, but knew they wanted something more flowery. The truth was that I didn't so much sell to people as meet them, engage their trust, then order take. It wasn't rocket science, it was quite straight forward really, barely deserving of congratulation or remuneration, I was fortunate enough to be selling what people wanted, any mug could do it. Nevertheless I responded to Norman's question in a manner expected of me, not wishing to disappoint my audience.

"I called Tony Burton, owner of Burton Haulage, every fortnight for four months before he agreed to go ahead with us. We were in competition with another bank but he appreciated the fact that I'd maintained contact and gave us the business. I kept regular contact with them and it paid off. That customer's worth ten grand a year to us now."

I could hear myself trotting this boastful guff out and felt embarrassed, self conscious, rather like catching a glimpse of yourself in the mirror when chatting someone up in a nightclub. Yes, I'd called on this company relentlessly but only because I knew the owner, he played golf at my club, and I'd ring every couple of weeks to arrange a game. And the only reason I'd benefited from their business was that no other bank would touch them.

I continued to press the right buttons as questions tumbled from Bob and Norman's repertoire, jumping though the hoops laid before me as the interview went on, embellishing my replies to the full but stopping short of the exaggeration that might render them unbelievable. It was like shooting fish in a barrel.

Norman – "Give an example of how you develop colleagues around you."

Me – "I mentored the new BDM, Robin, for his first few months with us." (A slight exaggeration, he became such a bleedin' nuisance after six weeks I ended up discreetly barring his calls).

Bob – "What personal targets do you set yourself?"

Me – "Every month I decide from which sector sales might come and strive to achieve, then exceed, stretching targets that I set for myself." (As if. I never knew where my next introduction was coming from. The only personal target I'd set was bringing my handicap down from 11 to 10 by the end of the year).

The interview ended with a flourish, with me detailing a quest to become the most successful salesman the bank had ever had, marginally falling short of issuing a blueprint for taking over the world. The bowlers had delivered a series of long hops which I had, with the minimum of fuss, crashed to the boundary, and with that, the three of us retired to a finger buffet of crustless sandwiches and mushroom vol-au-vents. A job well done.

Still basking in the reflective glory of my interview performance, I hadn't given any thought to the afternoon's event, the role play. I wasn't sure what to expect really, not having carried one out before but I didn't have long to wait. Norman presented me with a two page briefing once I'd scoffed my sandwiches, and led me to a small meeting room where I had fifteen minutes to study the hypothetical case of 'Smellies Bathroom Products'. Here my complacency ended. What the hell was this? Who in hell were 'Smellies Bathroom Products' and why was I reading a two page document about them, their brand and their products? All became clear when I turned to page two to find the following -

You are the National Sales Manager for Smellies Bathroom Products. Today you have a meeting with the Group Buyer for Lavish Hotels PLC, a chain boasting fifty hotel and leisure facilities across the UK. It is your objective to agree a twelve month contract to supply each of the sites with Smellies' shower gel, shampoo and soap products. Lavish Hotels PLC pride themselves on branding and have a reputation for associating themselves with luxury, high value products.

My heart sank, before reviving at pace as I considered what was written before me. What on earth was this? Terror took hold as I looked with anguish at page one, hoping I'd misread the document. Smellies Bathroom Products? I worked for a bank not a shampoo wholesaler. There must be some mistake. I'd heard of big organisations getting into psychometric testing and the like but what had inspired them to start selecting people via this kind of phoney baloney process? I could sell factoring facilities, end of story, there need be no mystery about it. I didn't need to prove myself by pretending to sell a box of Alberto Balsalm to Norman of the bank, this was ridiculous.

There wasn't time to find rhyme or reason for this turn of events, I was already three minutes into my fifteen minute allocation. I scanned the document for a second and third time, my mind filled with flashbacks to last minute swotting before school exams all those years ago. I'd read a sentence, look away, try to remember what it said, then panic when realising I'd forgotten it already.

I felt light headed. The comfort zone of the morning interview with its series of dolly catches had been rudely jettisoned to be replaced by the horror of a vacuous role play, a transparent and artificial scenario destined to make a mockery of me. My light headedness continued to the point where I felt removed from my own body, as if looking down on someone else in their private torment, yet knowing it was myelf I was looking down on. The hands on my wrist watch never moved so fast, ticking down as they did to the fateful fifteen minute mark. How could I be expected to digest all of this information about a company I'd never heard of, and products I barely used never mind understood, yet become expert enough to sell it to a hypothetical buyer in fifteen minutes flat? That buyer, by the way, being a colleague who knew as little about hotel chains as I did about shampoo. The whole situation was too surreal to comprehend, but it was real and with a knock on the door signalling only two minutes to go, I needed to come to terms with it pretty quickly.

The two minutes were up in what seemed like ten seconds as Bob swung open the door and invited me to accompany him to the adjoining office where Norman,… or rather Christopher Storey, Group Buyer of Lavish Hotels PLC, awaited. I felt like a condemned man taking his final steps to the nooseman, a not entirely unwelcome alternative such was the commotion of nerves jangling inside. I'd bowled them over this morning, why were they trying to trip me up now? The whole thing was ludicrous.

I followed Bob into the room and found Norman with his back to me, his hands clasped behind him as he rocked on his heels, chin held high, looking out of the window like a Sergeant Major deliberating over the merits of one final push over the top. Bob took a seat and sat scribbling notes in his role as assessor, he would remain silent while Norman conducted this section of the assessment.

Taking a deep breath but looking decidedly wild eyed, like Pacino before he shoots the police commander in The Godfather, I began. "Good morning Norman, I'm Alex Russon from,… .(mumbling) oh what was it again, (looks down at his notes) Lavish Hotels … no you're Lavish Hotels, I'm Shampoo Smellie Products… erm, how do you do?"

Great start. Norman was still to turn around. After what seemed like an eternity, he finally did. His opening salvo being rather more definite than mine.

"My name is Christopher Storey and I don't have much time. What is it you've come to see me about?".

Hell bells, what a welcome. Barely concealed disdain with more than a hint of aggression. I was on the back foot already. I had the presence of mind to remember the importance of rapport building, a classic ploy by the sales person to break down barriers and make the buyer more conducive to a discussion about the product on sale. It was in all the sales manuals. I was still extremely nervous though, and confused. I wanted to pass some idle time with this buyer who was purporting to be a stranger but it was impossible since I knew him so well. I knew for instance that he supported Newcastle United, had two kids, played guitar and drank beer for England. I'd scraped him off the pavement on Broad Street once after a heavy night's quaffing, yet now I was required to assume nothing about him at all. Added to this, I was fully aware they'd expect me to attempt some rapport building so when I enquired again about Norman's well being I was cut off at the knees with a no nonsense "Never mind that, let's get on with it" reply. It was designed to throw me off track. It worked. I hurriedly took my seat before realising I hadn't been invited to do so. I quickly rose again as Norman theatrically pulled a chair from beneath the table and sat on it as if the King of England at a coronation. I then sat, awkwardly.

Assuming that the notes Bob was writing may concern the issue of body language, I squared my shoulders to portray confidence but realised I might be looking like the Michelin Man so profoundly had I now stuck my chest out, so I relaxed my shoulders again. Leaning back in my chair, attempting to convey confidence, I reckoned this may be construed as slouching, so I leaned forward instead and clasped my hands together upon the table. I faced Norman directly but wondered if this was a little intense since he was also sitting forward, so I sat back and once more found myself in a quandary as to whether I appeared too slouched. Barely a word had been uttered and already I was in pieces, I felt any minute the men in white coats would enter to quietly drag me away, and I'd be grateful. The rest of my life in a padded cell was infinitely preferable to twenty minutes of this transparent torture. Opening my mouth to speak, it suddenly struck me that I had no words. The brain had not even started to form a sentence, how could my mouth be expected to? With my mouth hanging open wide like a gaping goldfish, I stared at Norman who stared back blankly for what seemed like an eternity. I'd completely corpsed, forgotten the product I was meant to be selling, the company I represented, the day of the week, the alphabet, my own name and whether I was male or female.

Norman continued to stare at me, not moving an inch to support me in my haggard state. Surely he could feel my pain? Apparently not, there wasn't a hint of empathy in his eyes, just a glint of impish pleasure, the rotten so and so appeared to be loving this. I turned helplessly towards Bob, yearning for a friendly smile or gesture of understanding, but got only a derisory sniff before he returned to his scribbling. Goodness knows what he was writing. This was fast becoming the most humiliating moment of my life, more humiliating even than my first tee fresh air shot before a hundred people in the Forfar Junior Open 1985.

Norman punctured the silence with a prompt.

"So, tell me Alex, what are you here for?"

"Yes, well, I represent a shampoo company who sell shampoo and… and… .other products too such as (reading notes) soaps and hair conditioners, erm, that have not been tested on animals."

" Yes?"

"And, well, I suppose… .well, would you be interested in buying some?"

Bob looked up from his notes and exchanged glances with Norman. In the 'How To Be An Effective Salesman' handbook they couldn't remember the bit where a salesman comes barging in, forgets the name of his company and without building rapport or adequately describing his organisation's products, barks out an apparent ultimatum. They were shocked, I was embarrassed.

This was the final straw, I could contain myself no longer.

"Look," this is hopeless. You've given me fifteen minutes to mug up on some made up company and I can't remember a thing about them. I'm pretending I don't know you when I do, and you're behaving like a ham actor in a production of An Inspector Calls. The whole thing's bizarre. Can you give me a few minutes before we carry on? I can't get my head around this at all."

"We're assessing several members of staff Alex and it would be unfair on them if we were to offer you preferential treatment. We'll have to ask you to carry on," replied Bob tersely, Norman nodding sagely in agreement.

The sorry affair dragged on for fifteen minutes more with me rallying slightly but not enough to retain any semblance of dignity, the entire conversation punctuated with pleas for me to be 'given a quick second' while I referred to my Smellies Bathroom Products factsheet, a piece of paper which for these twenty minutes of my life seemed like my only friend in the world, a life saving buoy in this choppiest of seas. Norman's face refused to crack despite the torture he knew he was discomforting me with, and he even kept a straight face when I, scrambling to exhibit some innovation, asked him if he believed there were any potential in fruit scented bidet fresheners. This was too much for Bob, who reached hurriedly for a glass of water with which to disguise his mirth. He spluttered uncontrollably, his eyes watering with hysterics.

Humiliated, stunned and winded, as if having taken a full tilt volley in the guts from Malcolm MacDonald, I dragged myself from the room once the agony had ended, and staggered to the kitchen for a coffee. This had been horrendous and I said as much when asked by Bob before I left the room, "How do you feel it went?" I'd answered very honestly, that it had been an uncomfortable, painful, dignity stripping exercise from start to finish and one I never wished to put myself through again. Indeed, as I closed the door on them, I did so symbolically in my own mind, vowing that if such a nightmare were necessary to make my way up the ladder in this company, I wanted nothing to do with it. I had been shocked at the savagery of this mugging and felt very sore indeed. They'd done nothing to prepare me sufficiently, nothing to ease my torment while it lasted, and subsequently shown no remorse when I'd challenged them on the fairness of this system, saying instead, "It's the same for everybody." Well it was wrong for everybody then, an unjust system that rewarded actors and pretenders instead of driving out the quality people who knew how to sell. People like me.

I skulked home and brooded for a day or two. I shared my feelings over the sorry affair with my boss, expecting sympathy and support but received neither. The company line was toed and despite the nudge, nudge, wink, wink attitude displayed by him when intimating the assessment day would be a formality, I now found this complacency had been unfounded and it was back to business as usual. My boss dropped me a short email confirming I'd flunked the assessment, but better luck next time. There'd be no next time, they could stick it. I couldn't care less about the stinking job, the career and all the trimmings that came with it; better car, few more quid, an extra day or two's holiday. If finding the next footing on the ladder meant performing like a circus clown I'd happily stay right where I was thank you very much. I suffered from enough humiliation being left for dead by eighteen year old centre forwards on a Saturday, I didn't need it at work as well.

CHAPTER TWENTY THREE

"... life feels so worthwhile when I go where you send me..."

I've come to the conclusion that I am an absolute heathen. I'm non-plussed by creatures in zoos while others bubble over with excitement, I'm bored at the Sea Life centre, fish of different shapes and sizes don't raise an eyebrow of interest, and history programmes leave me cold. Don't call me shallow, there's no need, I can do that myself. And it's good. It's a comfortable place to be, where the brain isn't extended and the memory bank remains free from minutiae overload. It's embarrassing when the every question posed by your children is returned with a shrug of the shoulders, but that's why I buy them encyclopedias for Christmas.

My brain can only deal with facts on a need to know basis, the average life span of a piranha fish I don't need to know for instance, while who won the FA Cup in 1957 I do (it was Villa by the way). I sense my children are beginning to despair, their questions no longer come thick and fast, more of a resigned dribble really, but paradoxically I feel I'm furthering their intelligence since they are required to seek out answers for themselves. Or am I just lazy?

With a weekend freed up because St Thomas had no fixture, I arranged to take Harry and Hattie to Scotland to see their Granny. Kate decided it was best not to put our six month old Emily through a seven hour drive twice in three days, so half of my family stayed at home while I took the other half north. This was likely to be our last visit to St Andrews, my Mum was relocating to Devon after spending fifteen years in this most attractive of Scottish coastal towns. Mum was born in Dundee, just a dozen or so miles north of St Andrews, and fell in love with the town from an early age when her parents took the family for days out at the seaside. I'd been to St Andrews many times when growing up in Stonehaven an hour or so away, I'd visited to play golf or spend a day on the beach watching Dad batter the ball miles, for us to fetch, during a two hour innings as we played beach cricket. But soon Mum was leaving town and heading five hundred and fifty miles south.

The car journey went without a hitch thanks to a DVD player borrowed from my colleague Len. Instead of seven hours worth of, "Are we there yet?" I heard only Girls Aloud and Grease from the rear of the car. I decided I'd make Len an offer he couldn't refuse for his DVD player, let me keep it or I'll tell your wife you'd left a dirty film in it.

Seven hours behind the wheel was shattering, so while I had a lie down upon our arrival at one o'clock, falling asleep on the spare bed, catching flies, Harry and Hattie sat down to make plans for the weekend with their Granny. The newly released Mr Bean film was on the agenda plus a trip to the Sea Life Centre, recently renamed 'The Aquarium' which we ended up at later that afternoon. If ever a place needed a lick of paint this was it, resembling as it did an ageing council owned sports and leisure centre that hadn't received a penny of funding in years and was being left to rot. A single member of staff was on hand to take money before returning to her Heat magazine, the rest of the place lay empty except for a few fish filled glass tanks and a seal pool attendant. We eked out a forty five minute tour before being invited, at the exit, to chalk a picture of a fish on an enormous blackboard, Harry and Hattie daubing creditable goldfish while I drew two fish fingers on a plate next to a collection of garden peas. Harry signed my picture ' ALEX – AGED NEARLY 40'. They love to remind me I'm getting old, but I don't need reminding, my fortieth hangs over me like a cloud about to burst. A walk along to the beach followed, a brief walk, the chill wind gusting in off the North Sea getting the better of us all. The car door slammed behind us without aid as we hunched into our seats and drove home where a warm fire and hot meal beckoned. It was Friday night, normally my Chinese take-away night but this time it'd be a Forfar bridie and a tin of baked beans, classic Scottish fare.

St Thomas may not have had a match the next morning but St Mary's did, a cup semi-final versus Rowley College. This was the biggest day in my former club's eight year history, beating hands down the Charity Cup success two years prior which was nothing more than a makeweight of a competition. The 2nd division that year was reduced to just a handful of teams and to boost the number of fixtures a ' Charity Cup' was introduced for one season only, and St Mary's were the last team standing. As silverware went, this trophy didn't deserve Duraglit treatment or even a spit and polish, perhaps just a dusting down when someone remembered it was in the cupboard. But today St Mary's found themselves in the last four of THE cup, win this and the final would be held at non-league Halesowen Town's floodlit ground before hundreds of people, St Mary's would have hit the big time and Burberry suits could justifiably be ordered. In the week leading up to the game I texted my best wishes to captain Nick Sprason and manager Jack, both replied with questions about their semi-final opponents. They were facing a team from our second division, a team we'd played just three weeks before and they wanted some pointers. Of course a serious outfit would have posted scouts to our fixture against Rowley but instead they were relying on my say so, such an amateurish approach left them wide open to sabotage and this I considered. Should I tell them of a mystical four man front line complete with Alan Shearer having been brought back from retirement because he was a family friend of the manager? Maybe I could invent a bizarre two man defensive formation that would persuade St Mary's to load their attack and leave themselves exposed at the back? No, I couldn't muster the courage to spoil their big day with poor quality pranks that didn't stand an earthly of being believed, so I informed them of the brutish centre forward we had faced and his unfeasibly long throw-ins. In addition I described a well drilled, organised team who should not be taken for granted simply because they were in the second division. St Mary's clearly paid attention, booking their place in the final with a one nil victory after extra time. It was obvious how much they were missing their lumbering, static centre back of seasons past. If sabotage had been my aim, I'd have stayed on at St Mary's for another season, they'd have been out in the preliminary round.

Harry returned from his trip to the beach with his Granny, jeans soaked to the knee, Hattie with a bucket of shells and a big smile, her afternoon mapped out: washing sea shells and gluing them to cardboard to produce a collage. This would have to wait until after the cinema though, Mr Bean and his rubbery face awaited as did possibly the rudest ticket kiosk attendant we'd had the misfortune to meet, wordlessly collecting our cash and returning tickets without eye contact. She was too busy texting a presumably despairing husband who'd be trying to enjoy an afternoon away from his sourpuss wife. I told her what I thought of her attitude and only then was she moved to look at me, or glower to be more accurate.

"Four hundred miles the kids have travelled to watch this film with their Granny, and we get you for a welcome. Thanks a lot."

A friend of mine, Greig, who lived just a few miles down the coast, drove up on the Saturday evening to have tea with us. I've known him since the late 80's when our mutual devotion to Depeche Mode brought us together and we've been in touch ever since. I feel our dedication to Depeche Mode deserves more explanation but don't have the patience to describe the circumstances in a manner that makes either of us look cool, so I won't bother. Although I lived in Birmingham at the time Greig and I met, his proximity to my mother's house enabled us to meet most times I visited Scotland. He duly demolished the majority of mother's cottage pie, inflicted similar damage to her choice ice-cream then bid me farewell until the following weekend when he'd be down for Emily's baptism at St Thomas. I recommended he buy Gruff Rhys' new album, he suggested I try Feeder's, both of us nodded as if we'd take the other up on the recommendation, both knowing neither of us would. For years we'd been trading band names but not once had either of us acted on the 'heads up' given by the other, it had become a tradition.

After a second consecutive unbroken nights sleep, no Emily to wake me, I awoke to hear my Mum beavering away in the kitchen, pans clattering and bacon crackling, breakfast was on its way. I sat down to a plate brimming with every traditional fried breakfast item you can think of, with some haggis to top it off. Harry wanted only egg and sausage, Hattie egg and bacon, their pickiness with food a trait I'd been trying to shake them from for years but unsuccesfully. My brothers and I used to devour pretty much anything put before us, these two were fussy eaters. I offered them some of my tomato or fried bread but they were having none of it, and Hattie positively wretched when I suggested she try some black pudding. I polished off the lot and headed for church while they prepared for another visit to the beach, it was a much warmer day today and the West Sands would be teeming with Sunday walkers.

Church was different. I went to Hope Park, a Church of Scotland establishment in the town, and found a congregation of perhaps two hundred or so in this old fashioned church with its pews and high pulpit. The rector was all robed up, unlike our vicar who dresses in a manner that suggests he is in fact a human being like the rest of us, and delivered his message in cheerless manner. Apart from a sprinkling of Sunday best attired children, I was the youngest in the church by approximately twenty years, the pews a sea of grey hair and bald heads with walking sticks littering the two gangways. The hymns were mostly of the ancient variety and as for interaction between the rector and his flock, there was none. It was a wholly different feel to the services I'd become used to at St Thomas which are never a one man show where you simply pin back your ears and listen. I'd become accustomed to a lighter experience, God and His teaching very much at the heart of the service, but not delivered in a grim, cheerless fashion that seems to take all of the love out of the message. Nevertheless, it was interesting to experience a different type of service and I enjoyed it despite the rather stuffy feel, the rector may have presented his sermon as if he were nursing haemorrhoids but still there was a message, there's always a message.

I've sat through oodles of teeth clenchingly dull sermons but never have I come away feeling there wasn't significance somewhere in there, even the rotten sermons have meaning, and today I learned that choosing God is the choice of no-one else but ourselves. The sermon hinged on Pilate's exchange with Jesus when Pilate is trying to decide what to do about this man brought before him. With the crowd baying for Jesus's crucifixion, Pilate is bewildered about who Jesus is and asks him face to face. Jesus answers "Who do you say I am?" Never mind other people he suggests, where is your faith at? Do you believe in God Almighty or not? The rector may have been dull but this was a message I was happy to take away, a reminder that it's a one to one relationship with God, not a group hug or social club that we engage in only to lose the true meaning of what being a Christian is the moment we leave church on a Sunday. It's about believing that Jesus is God's son put on earth to die so that we can be put right with God and that by putting your faith in Him, your life can be filled with peace. Bit of a sermon that in itself, sorry. Maybe I should become a vicar, better still a rector at Hope Park where I can loosen things up a bit.

I caught up with Harry, Hattie and Mum at the beach and was roped into digging a tunnel from the wet sand down to the seashore a few yards away. I wanted to talk to my children about the subject of futility but thought this might ruin their fun, so duly spent a half hour with them, digging sand before watching on as our work was flattened by the incoming tide. With a 375 mile drive ahead of me, I couldn't enjoy our seaside high jinks, I just wanted to get on the road when I had so far to travel. With nine penalty points sitting on my licence I'd need to travel sedately so a minimum seven hour journey was on the cards. Mum dragged Harry off the beach, his jeans matted once again with wet sand and his trainers squelching with sea water, Hattie and I waited in the car, discussing which DVD she'd be watching on the way home. I had Bob Dylan 'Unplugged' in the boot if she was fed up of Grease. She declined.

We left St Andrews possibly for the final time. With the town being well sought after by retiring couples, minted students and golf mad American billionaires, Mum's house was bound to sell quickly. It'd be a sad day when she left this town, it had always been a wonderful haven for the rest of the family. We'd visit my Mum wherever she lived but it was a bonus that she lived at the home of golf, in a vibrant old town free of modern day commercialisation. It was a busy yet tranquil place, unspoilt by progress. Devon had its attractions but The Old Course, West Sands, fudge doughnuts and stovies weren't amongst them.

CHAPTER TWENTY FOUR

"… you're the future and I'm with you…"

To fish or not to fish, that is the question. I'm not talking about taking a rod and nets down to the canal to fish for shopping trolleys and used contraceptives, I'm thinking about affixing the Christian symbol of a fish to the rear windscreen of my car and I'm undecided.

The case against :

Isn't there a certain smugness to displaying the fish symbol? I wonder if it conveys an 'I'm all right Jack' kind of message. While all you fellow drivers struggle on with your lives I can hang my nose in the air cos I'm a Christian. I worry too that it suggests I'm part of an exclusive club, you're either in or you're out with God, I'm in because I have a fish, you're out because all you've got is a 'babe on board' sticker. Does it suggest a holier than thou attitude to life, a 'my life is considerably more worthy than yours' kind of deal? And why feel the need to display a Christian symbol? Jesus is in your heart, perhaps a gimmicky sticker trivialises Christianity in some way.

The case for :

Becoming a Christian has changed my life and I want to shout it from the rooftops. You can get banged up for something like that, so perhaps an outward display of faith such as this is a good substitute? Many young people today see Christianity as irrelevant, would the sight of a thirty something proudly declaring his faith make it more relevant, thought provoking, if only for a minute? Don't hide your light under a bushel so we're told in the bible, be a light to shine across the world. Surely it'd be a good witness to my children if no-one else, that God is such a central part of my life that I'm happy for everyone to know it, it will teach them not to hide away from faith, it is OK to believe in God, whatever their friends may say.

Harry and Hattie saw the coloured fish symbol that my friend Peter had bought me, it was sitting on the dashboard still safely in its packet.

"What's that Daddy?"

"It's a fish, a sort of badge that people have on their cars to tell people they believe in Jesus."

"I thought a cross meant that?"

"Yes it does, but a fish like this is a symbol too".

"Oh," Hattie's mind ticked over for a minute, she wasn't going to let things rest there.

"But why do people put them on their cars?"

I turned my music off so I could concentrate on my answer, if Harry and Hattie were inquisitive about this subject, I didn't want to goof a response.

"I suppose to tell everyone who sees it that they believe in God and are proud to do so." Judging by Hattie's expression this answer was wholly inadequate.

"But... why do they want people to know they believe in God?" she said, Harry turned to face me, eager to hear a decent response to this question, he appeared to have been thinking the same thing. Crikey, I was under pressure now!

"Well put it this way. When I'm driving along and feeling a bit fed up, maybe something's gone wrong at work and I'm a bit grumpy, if I drive past a car with a fish badge on it, I feel happier straight away. It reminds me that God is there for me and whatever is happening in my life, big problems or small, He's there to look after me".

I looked in my rear view mirror for Hattie's reaction and was glad to see her nod her understanding and smile, apparently content with her Dad's explanation. Harry added, "Yeah, so it puts a smile on your face and you forget all your troubles don't you Daddy?" I nodded. My mind was made up, this was all the confirmation I needed that fish badges on cars were a good thing and after we'd eaten the picnic that we were driving to the park to scoff, we returned to the car to attach the sticker onto the rear windscreen together. It wouldn't do my driving any harm, having clocked up nine points for speeding, perhaps there was less chance of a ban inducing caution if I had the responsibility of being a Christian etched on my rear window.

... ...

St Thomas' football season was limping to a finish. It had been three weeks since our last match, training sessions had been sporadic during this time and with us having nothing to play for in our remaining two fixtures, there was a sense that the season had finished already. It was mathematically impossible for us to gain promotion unless one of the three teams above us fielded half a dozen ineligible players, burnt down an away dressing room and beat up the referee, perhaps then they'd be docked sufficient points for us to overtake them, but we had to accept that this was somewhat unlikely.

We may not have been playing much footie but here had been plenty of football to watch, Easter had been and gone with wall to wall football on television to keep us entertained. Walsall were confirmed as promoted, three English clubs qualified for the semi finals of the Champions League, and the new Wembley was promised a Chelsea v Manchester United FA Cup final (which seemed rather convenient, commentators speculated whether the balls in the bag when the draw was made for the semi-final had been doctored in some way, two ice blocks and a couple of hot potatoes perhaps). Villa had conformed to tradition by winning a couple of games late on in the season to avoid relegation and I'd taken Harry and Hattie to the Easter Monday bore draw against Wigan where an early sending off for our opponents saw them put ten men behind the ball for the remainder of the game. A spectacle it wasn't.

I'd been to my first WMCFL league meeting during this three week break from playing. These meetings are held in Halesowen at the Zion Christian Centre and representatives from every club are expected to attend or the club faces a fine, seems fair enough. After a couple of wrong turns I turned up at the same time as John Myatt, a friend of mine from the St Mary's team and a centre back whom I'd taught all he knew. That's why he was on the bench these days. He'd never been to a league meeting either but had decided now would be an opportune time to start. St Marys were playing in the cup final soon and there was a scrap going on for selection, a touch of brown nosing to the management would do his chances no harm.

The room where the meeting was held was effectively the Christian

Centre's canteen, spacious enough but I don't expect Bert Millichip used to chair FA meetings with the smell of fried bacon wafting across his nostrils. A row of trestle tables had been put out from where the six members of the commitee would address the twenty or so club representatives perched on two rows before them. I recognised several faces, mostly managers and team captains, but there were a few unfamiliar, grumpy looking faces too, most likely players taking their turn to attend the meeting while their mates embarked on their Friday night session. The committee filed in, took their seats, and the meeting was opened by Neil Kovacs, League Secretary, who invited Ed Walker, E-Secretary, to open in prayer so the meeting could commence.

It felt like a throwback to the trade union days of the 70's, or at least what I perceive meetings of that type to have been like. It was pin back your ears and listen time while each member of the committee took turns to speak about their area of responsibility within the league. Tony Skelton, Disciplinary Officer, delivered the poor disciplinary statistics for the season to date and rightly expressed his disappointment over this while congratulating Selly Oak for their determined efforts to address their disciplinary problems internally, they'd suspended six players for continual indiscretions themselves rather than rely solely on the league's suspension system. Ed Walker explained that the deadline was fast approaching for new applications from clubs wanting to join the league and was pleased to announce there were two or three very likely, he also confirmed that the website will now show a disciplinary league table (I took a peek when I got home to find St Thomas miles ahead at the top). James Oratayo, Fixtures Secretary, had nothing to add other than to confirm he was stepping down and a new Fixtures Secretary needed to be found for the following season and Dave Davies representing the referees, explained there was a dearth of referees and did anyone want to train up? There was much shuffling in seats and harrumphing but no takers, although Ed Walker was rumoured to be showing an interest. Dave told us that of the thirty refs to start the season, many had drifted away leaving a nucleus of around sixteen which presented problems if the league were to be sustained. He also reminded us that the treatment of referees needed improving, too many cautions were for dissent, cut this out and the statistics would look a whole lot better, his glare fixing on my side of the room at this juncture.

Neil Kovacs, League Secretary and manager of last years league champions Chawn Hill, was eager to promote the forthcoming end of season awards night. For a fiver a head, a night of fun and frolickery was promised at Birchley Social Club when teams would be recognised for their achievements during the season and individual players for their performances and goal scoring records. I was tempted to stick my hand up and ask if there could be a special award this year for 'most megged centre back', perhaps I might then stand a chance of silverware, or maybe 'most garish strip of the season' in which case St Thomas would win hands down. Neil was hoping for a turnout of around two hundred for awards night but couldn't promise the fifty he'd brought from Chawn Hill last year since they'd not be winning the league this season, I reckoned there'd be a minimum fifty from St Mary's if they won the cup, that's if they weren't still in Halesowen Town's dressing rooms celebrating.

I'd been looking forward to the 'Any Other Business' section at the end of the meeting, I thought it might tempt some indignation from someone who'd come along with a bee in their bonnet, but to my disappointment it passed without a word. There were to be no fireworks, Neil asked me to close in prayer which I did, fumbling through having been caught on the hop not expecting to be asked. Praying in public has always been something I struggle with, you get tongue tied and self conscious, but it's all good, it's what you're saying in your heart to God that matters, it's not a problem if you verbalise inadequately.

I'd become similarly stage struck when speaking at Emily's baptism the Sunday prior. I'd given a five minute talk explaining why Kate and I felt it important that Emily should be baptised and inviting all people in the congregation to consider their relationship, if any, with God. It was pretty daunting having almost every member of our family, plus dozens of good friends, sitting in silence while I spoke about our Christian faith. Not all would be in agreement and I knew some would find the whole subject uncomfortable, but while many baptisms are carried out as more of a social function rather than a Christian centred ceremony, I was eager to explain to everyone just how important Kate and I felt this occasion was. I didn't get heckled, but Harry and Hattie sat in the front row grinning at me the whole time, tickled by the sight of their Dad suddenly turning into a public orator.

The league meeting ended with Neil Kovacs handing me two trophies. I was flattered, until he explained they were for my team mate Mark Hadden who hadn't collected them since being named Player Of The Season and Top Goalscorer last season. I walked back to the car clutching my trophies, hoping passers by might see me, but there was no-one but John Myatt on hand, ribbing me for getting closer to a trophy than I had any right to. We said our goodbyes, I turned up The Wedding Present on my car stereo and set off for home. Thirty seconds later I was doing a three point turn, I'd driven down a cul-de-sac.

We were playing Walsall Olympic today, rock bottom in their first season in the league, but fresh off the back of their very first victory, in midweek, after sixteen outings. They'd beaten Brierley Hill, our conquerors a couple of games ago, by the comprehensive scoreline of three nil. We weren't overly concerned. We'd shown an improved attitude in the recent game and the short journey to our former home Anchor Meadow made it feel like a home game, plus it'd be a pressure free atmosphere now that promotion was out of the window. I was looking forward to it, though with an amount of apprehension. The only exercise I'd had in the three weeks since the last match was a game of golf and a climb up the stairs, that was about it. If I was to face yet another speed merchant half my age, I was doomed. That's if I was picked, I'd not been training in ages due to other commitments on Tuesday nights – babysitting Emily, a church meeting and an overnight stay with work. In my St Mary's days, a succession of missed training sessions spelt your demotion to the bench, but St Thomas didn't operate along these lines, they couldn't afford to, so much smaller was the squad.

Talking of St Mary's, Cup Final fever had most assuredly taken hold. The game was only five days away and their preparation had begun. Two additional training sessions had been organised after our manager Rob Hill tipped them off that the pitch where the final was being played was enormous, way bigger than any in our league, stamina would be a vital factor. Rob had also pointed out that the half-time break needed addressing. When St Thomas had reached the Cup Final a few years back, they'd returned to the dressing room at half-time having conceded a late goal in the first half, and instead of taking a slug of water, having a quick breather then going back out as we do in league fixtures, they'd got the full fifteen minute interval to fill and didn't know how to cope with it. Apparently there'd been utter silence and a plummeting of morale as bewildered team-mates, disorientated by their surroundings and the length of time they had to wait for the resumption, slowly began to freeze. Rob suggested St Mary's address this possibility though he knew not how, I suppose a three nil lead at half-time would help.

A coach to the game for players and supporters was being organised. It was hoped the standard away support of two would be boosted by an entourage of family and friends, and with St Mary's having good links with Aldridge Parish Church I expected there'd be a good following. I was certainly going, I couldn't wait. It was the perfect scenario for me, watching my former team playing the biggest match of their lives but me feeling detached enough now to enjoy it. Rather than yearning to be on the pitch, which had I stayed at St Mary's I'm sure I would be, my backside full of splinters from the substitutes' bench, I could look on from the terraces and feel none of the pressure that they would no doubt be feeling. The throne in the dressing room would surely receive some fearful damage pre-kick off, there'd be an orderly queue from the moment the team coach arrived. Tickets for the final weren't unreasonably priced at a princely two quid, the burgers would probably cost more than that, and the game was to commence at 7.45pm, plenty of time for me to scoff my tea and drive across to Halesowen Town's floodlit ground. My Dad used to walk me past there in my pram as a kid, little did I know then that I'd one day return to see the mighty St Mary's take on Renewal Solihull in the biggest Cup Final since The Dog & Duck played The Navigation in the West Midlands Alehouses Of No Repute League Cup Final, the night before.

But back to matters at home, St Thomas versus Walsall Olympic, as meaningless a contest as you could hope to find with neither team having anything to play for. Nevertheless, we needed to start building now for the next season and a comprehensive victory wouldn't be a bad place to start. What was a bad place to start was this rotten pitch. We'd had ten days of unseasonally hot weather, with no rain to soften a bone hard Anchor Meadow pitch which was now better suited to tap dancing. A couple of the players wore trainers rather than studs, Daz Smail being one, wearing a powder blue pair that had no right to be on a football field whatsoever. Had a woman been wearing them down at Fitness First you might have understood, but this was a game of football, for men. I wore studs, and clattered across the pitch during the warm-up sounding like a horse leaving the paddock.

There was very much an end of season feel to the game. Walsall appeared de-mob happy as they waited for the game to begin, half of them enjoying a game of tig while the remainder sat around chatting as they basked in the sun. We were more relaxed than usual, Daz's bright blue trainers providing much of the conversation as we prepared for the game in time honoured fashion, crowding into the penalty box awaiting crosses from both flanks. The pressure was off, the atmosphere amongst us was good, the game kicking off with a healthy crowd of perhaps twenty enjoying the sunshine. I was playing centre back alongside Nick Jones since Chris Preece was still troubled by injury and on the substitutes bench, Clem was away with the school on a weekend break. Nick suggested we played a sweeper system between us rather than a zonal game where he'd play right side and me left. I said okay. This was a mistake. Disorientated and playing a system I'd never before played, I proceeded to play the shocker of all shocking shockers, but more of that later.

There was an inevitability about this game within ten minutes of it commencing. Walsall Olympic weren't bottom of the league for nothing, they had been gubbed left, right and centre throughout the season and their midweek victory was clearly a blip. We were kicking downhill in the first half and set up camp there for the majority of the opening forty five minutes. Despite the rock hard surface allowing the ball to bobble around like a golf ball trying to roll on concrete, our passing was excellent as we ran rings around the opposition, cutting through them like a knife through butter and all those other footballing cliches that you know so well. Mark Hadden headed us into the lead early on, and midfielder for the day, Joe Lister, slid a second into the corner before adding a third moments later having obliged the familiar cry from Preecey of "Rhino!" Joe's a sturdy individual, you wouldn't want to get in the way of him when he's at full tilt, so when he does the 'Rhino', pawing the earth with the ball at his feet, steam blowing out of his ears before setting off on a run with his head down, all scatter before him, to get in the way would be folly of the highest order. He barged his way forward, exchanged a one-two with Matt Brady and slid the ball into the net. No-one ventured a tackle, they valued their innards too much.

We were cantering at three nil after twenty odd minutes, it was already game over. Rob in goal had little to do, the midfield had almost complete possession of the ball, and the strikers were taking potshots at will. The second half followed a similar pattern to the first, total domination, and the final score of 5-1 was not flattering, Joe Lister completing his hat-trick with Mark Hadden adding another to his huge tally for the season. With Ian Pearsall waiting one more week before reappearing for St Thomas, it was down to Matt Challoner to collect the customary booking, though he was rather hard done by considering it was for retaliation after the guy marking him nearly took his head off with a kung fu style challenge. Quite honestly I'd like to leave the match report there, you've read all you need to know, we won and that's it, but it'd be dishonest of me not to confess to my jaw droppingly poor display, so here goes.

You've heard of career threatening injuries? Well this was a career threatening performance, the sort that has a player shaking his head in disbelief and wondering, after ninety minutes of mistakes, whether this really is a sporting pursuit best suited to him. Golfers amongst you may sympathise. There are times when you step off the course utterly humiliated, having spent four hours shanking, duffing, pulling and topping, your playing partners slowly going silent on you, leaving you to retreat into a private state of trauma. I've seen someone throw their clubs into the lake during a round of golf before now, well you can't very well stalk off the football pitch refusing to continue, but looking back I should have pulled the shirt off my back, thrown my hooves into the bin and put everyone out of their misery.

Where do I start? Well the beginning I suppose, or the opening ten minutes during which time I didn't touch the ball once. "Make your first touch a good touch," so they say, well by the time mine came the rest of the team had passed, tackled or shot the ball ten times over, the thing had come nowhere near me. And when it did, it was in the form of a square pass from Daz at left back which I was supposed to heave forward, instead it bobbled over my swinging foot and into the path of an opponent. Not to worry, he did nothing with it, no harm done. A minute later I had another opportunity, an aimless through ball from Walsall leaving me ages of time to mop up, but I simply couldn't bring the ball under control as it bounced around evading my lunges, and by the time I did bring it under, a striker had closed me down and picked my pocket. Thankfully, he fluffed his resultant shot at goal, screwing wide enough for it almost to go for a throw-in which I hoped might take the focus off my blunder. I took a deep breath, reached down to pull up my socks, as if that was going to make any difference, and ambled forward to wait for the goal kick. Rob scuffed it and it came straight to me, another chance to redeem myself. Did I take it? Did I heck. I 'trapped' the ball about twenty yards as it bounced off my ankle and into the path once again of the very same centre forward who must have thought his birthdays had all come at once, again however he let me off the hook, or rather Nick Jones did as he swooped to sweep up after me. This was getting embarrasing, everyone in the team was playing well, stroking the ball about as if gracing a Premiership fixture and I was the odd one out, stinking the place up with miscontrol and dither.

It got worse. After about half an hour, with us three nil up, I sprinted after another through ball of theirs only for a young winger to whip me for pace and shoot narrowly wide despite starting the chase a good five yards behind me. Two minutes later, a huge punt forward by their keeper plunged from the sky towards my advancing pate and I misjudged it hopelessly, receiving the ball full in the face and tumbling to the ground. Was it my imagination or were spectators laughing? No, I don't think it was my imagination, this was becoming cringeworthy. But then, finally, after my every involvement had been one of profound haplessness, a success! Walsall moved forward and released a pass to the left winger who I steamed across the pitch in pursuit of. He was fast, but my shame brought out a never previously seen burst of pace, and as he prodded the ball in front of himself, bearing down on goal, I screamed in with a last ditch slide tackle that despatched the ball out of play and him onto his backside. At last, I'd done something worthy of my selection, what a relief. Probably out of a feeling of shock, my team-mates offered words of sympathetic congratulation and encouragement, and I awaited the throw-in with my shoulders a little less slumped than before... .but... my nadir was just seconds away. From the resultant throw-in, the very same winger drifted past Andy Carter, slid a square ball across our six yard box and my outstretched leg converted it into the top corner of the net. My humiliation was complete. Thirty five minutes of death defying ineptitude and now this, a ludicrous own goal that had the spectators in stitches. I looked around for words of comfort from my team-mates, perhaps an "unlucky Al," or a "Nothing you could do mate," but found my orange shirted comrades avoiding eye contact and offering not a word of consolation, they were gonna let me stew. Half-time couldn't come quick enough.

The second half was marginally less catastrophic than the first as far as my performance went. The team played brilliantly and coasted to victory, but I felt like Roy Keane must have when forced to sit out the Champions League Final when Man United won it, glorious achievement for the team, but an empty feeling for himself. The fun seemed to be going on around me and when I did get a chance to join in, I wished I hadn't. When I shepherded through balls back to my keeper, the striker nicked it off me. When I rose to head a ball clear, it flew over my head. If I attempted a pass, I'd send it out of play or to an opponent's feet. I was truly dire. By the time Joe Lister castigated me for wailing a ball upfield instead of passing, "ALEX! CALM IT MATE, YER JUST LUMPIN' IT!" I couldn't care less, I was just chuffed to have made contact with the damned thing. Chris Preece came on shortly into the second half and we reverted to a more zonal system which made me feel a little more confident, but I had no grounds to be, the rickets kept coming. At one point I was in acres of space on the left wing when Buzz turned to spray a ball out wide to me, but the moment he realised it was me and not Matt Challoner over there, he thought better of it and played it into trouble up the right instead. And I couldn't blame him.

Hey ho. Good days and bad days, but the bad days were beginning to outnumber the good for this thirty something. Daz's blue trainers gleaming in the sunlight gave me a laugh, as did the sight of Chris Preece coming on in driver's gloves despite the 21 degrees heat. Winning 5-1 was great news too, but all in all there had to be questions about the sanity of me continuing with competitive football if this was the best I could do. What was the footballing equivalent of a P45? Whatever it was, I sensed Rob was planning one for me.

CHAPTER TWENTY FIVE

The WMCFL Cup Final
St Mary's FC v Renewal Solihull
7.45pm April 25th 2007
at Halesowen Town FC
Admission £2

Wow! The FA Cup Final of the West Midlands Christian Football League, to be held under floodlights at Halesowen Town's ground, where there were terraces, proper seats and everything. You had to enter through a turnstile! You paid to go in! There were match programmes, tannoy announcers, mascots, the lot. This was billy big time football and no mistake. For St Marys and Renewal Solihull, a one time only step into the world of semi-professional football played before paying spectators, a night that promised memories grandchildren of the future could be bored to tears by. I was excited and I was only spectating.

The fixture coincided with the Champions League semi-final between Chelsea and Liverpool so the attendance was dented by a poor neutrals turnout, but given the choice between Drogba tumbling to the floor under the challenge of a stray butterfly or watching two genuine amateur football teams scrapping it out in the games of their lives, I was more than happy paying a couple of quid in Halesowen rather than sitting on the sofa to berate the television set. A couple of hundred turned up on a bright but chilly Spring evening, two camps soon forming between the followers of the finalists, St Marys hardcore support of mates, ex-players and former managers took to the terrace on the halfway line, while Renewal Solihull's supporters arranged their posteriors in the seats opposite, some stood further down the terrace from St Mary's support. There was a sprinkling of neutrals but most attendees appeared to have a vested interest.

It was great to be standing on a terrace again after years of the Premiership's cosseting seats. I missed the freedom of the terracing where you could stretch your legs a bit, jump on the spot if you were cold and rub shoulders with fellow supporters in an atmosphere of camaraderie. Tonight I was sandwiched between my former manager Gareth Powell (who asked me if I'd arrived on time for a tackle since he last saw me) and Rob Hill my current manager (who knew the answer but was too polite to say). We looked on alongside former players Dennis, Denny, Dan, Clem and many other friends of the team, our huddle of thirty odd in good spirits as we awaited the players arrival. Two buglers blowing for all their worth behind one of the goals, heralded the entrance of the two teams who filed onto the pitch from the dressing rooms beneath. Nick Sprason, captain of St Marys, was in his element, living the dream as he loosed hands with his four year old mascot and began his side stepping exercises before reaching for a couple of imaginary headers, he'd been watching too much Champions League on the telly. The two teams lined up on the halfway line to face the seated spectators and smiled for the camera, all taking the trouble to do the things proper footballers do; run on the spot, swivel their hips, chew gum and look menacing while an announcer read out their names. When they broke to warm up at their respective ends, a shock. Darren Moore was kicking about with Renewal's squad! Had they secured the last minute big money signing of Derby County's captain to bolster their cup chances? This was quite a coup, I didn't fancy St Mary's centre-forward Jackaman's chances against a speedy man mountain who until this week was on the threshold of Premiership football with Derby County. I was mistaken, Jack could rest easy, Darren Moore had been invited along purely as chief motivator by a member of Renewal Solihull who apparently knew him well, he'd take no part in the match. St Marys' chief motivator was Gareth Powell their former manager, less pedigree than Darren Moore but twice as frightening. Never mind Fergy, if you wanted hair drier treatment Gareth would leave you bald after thirty seconds.

The pitch had clearly enjoyed a full season's football. Dried out, bony, and looking somewhat sorry for itself, it was still better than any surface we normally played on in the league. I used to take a peek at this pitch when I was two years old and being walked by my father all those years ago. We lived in Halesowen then and on a weekend he'd take me for a wander to hear the football match going on, though not taking me inside in case Halesowen Town put me off following the Villa in later life. One of my earliest memories is of us walking past the turnstiles and me looking through to try and see what was happening on the other side of them, I could hear shouting and wanted to know what the noise was. The promise of an ice cream was normally enough to drag me away, tonight not even the promise of Champions League football at it's finest could keep me away though, I was well excited.

St Marys' had purchased a new kit especially for the occasion, a pillar box red affair with the keeper in an equally garish green. Had St Thomas been their opponents, I wished, the clash of eye squinting orange versus an unsightly red would have been too hideous to contemplate but Renewal Solihull brought order to proceedings with a plain blue and white strip, although I found this equally as offensive. It looked like a Birmingham City kit. Had I been a neutral tonight, I wouldn't have been for long.

There was a party atmosphere amongst the spectators that contrasted with the brick inducing apprehension of the players. We were out for a good night's entertainment, they were shrinking visibly as we looked on, nerves apparently gripping them all. Some stood waving to family, others joshed nervously with one another, others still looked sternly at the floor, their hearts in their mouths. This was a big occasion for them, they'd have talked of nothing else since qualifying for the final a month ago and now here it was. They wanted to do themselves justice, they didn't want to let down their team-mates, they just wanted this game to start so the nerves could subside. They didn't have to wait long, referee Andrew Dixon blew his whistle and we were off.

The early stages had the ball ping ponging from one eighteen yard box to the other. Defenders with the ball at their feet were fearful of a mistake so simply launched it forward to their opposite numbers who had the same concerns and heaved it straight back again. Strikers scurried around to put pressure on worried defenders, midfielders could only stand and watch as the ball continuously sailed over their heads into the darkening sky. The game had commenced without need for floodlights but they were turned on after ten minutes and this seemed to act as a signal for the game to calm down and start properly.

Immediately, the first goal was scored. A cross from the left saw Josh Blunt head the ball into a diving keeper's arms only for the goalie to fumble it over the line having seemingly had it under control. 1-0 St Mary's. The applause was somewhat muted since no-one appeared to realise the ball had dribbled over the line until the ref pointed to the centre circle. St Mary's joy was shortlived, a Renewal equaliser crashing in three minutes later thanks to a spectacular volley from twenty five yards. This was becoming a good game, I'd expected a war of attrition with two worried sides concentrating on damage limitation, but we were being treated to an entertaining game of footie.

There were no further goals in the first half but plenty more goalmouth incident, chances galore at both ends. I headed off for a sausage roll from the refreshment cabin and sat inside to keep the chill away, it had turned into a cold evening. I sat alone, listening to people as they queued and chatted, a number of faces I recognised from other clubs in the league, like me they'd chosen to leave Schevchenko and co to their own devices and support the WMCFL instead, and good on them. The seemingly interminable half-time interval went on, and on, and on. I had time to bury my large sausage roll and get up to order a second before returning to my spot on the terraces alongside a shivering Denny and Fairbank, both regretting their 'straight from work' office attire as they hunched their shoulders into open necked shirts, hands deep in their trouser pockets.

The buglers returned the players to the arena and we were away again. In fact the buglers didn't stop throughout the game, creating an atmosphere in their own way that made the match more of an occasion. And then on the hour mark, Dave Bignall set them off on a musical frenzy when he volleyed in from close range after a free-kick had been nodded on to the back post where he was lurking. 2-1 St Mary's. Again the lead was shortlived, a scrappy equaliser turned in by Renewal after a couple of panicked attempts to clear the ball from the goalmouth. This match was justifying the two quid entrance fee, end to end with a little bit of needle creeping in for good measure. Sprason had been singled out by the Renewal support as public enemy number one following a couple of questionable challenges and knowing how he winds opponents up on the pitch, he'd soon be making enemies there too I didn't doubt. He's one of these irritating, not dirty, but irritating midfielders who just happens to catch you a little bit late in the tackle, pulls your shirt before rising for a header, tells you you're rubbish when you make a mistake, that sort of thing. Opponents want to lynch him, team-mates though are thankful because he takes all the unwanted attention of headstrong opposing players while you get on with your own game. I suppose every team has a Sprason, a player who other teams can't stand but your team are glad of, particularly when he conjures up a goal such as the one he notched tonight with twenty minutes of the game remaining.

The game had continued to be an enthralling end to end affair, both teams attacking, cheered on by increasingly frantic supporters. Renewal seemed to have brought with them a gaggle of schoolgirls, their support being of a much higher, shrill pitch than the deep throated St Mary's bellowings. Each time they broke over the halfway line it was cotton wool in ears time until Sprason silenced them with a goal that he'll talk about, and believe me he will talk about, for the rest of his life. A sustained St Mary's attack put Renewal under intense pressure until they appeared to have cleared their lines, the ball breaking out of defence towards Sprason's right boot. Those of us who have seen his efforts with said right boot, will appreciate just how safe the ball was in that area of the pitch, the last time he took a shot with it he kicked fresh air and landed in a heap on the floor. But not tonight. In a carbon copy of the first Renewal goal, Sprason clattered the ball low and hard into the far corner. 3-2 St Mary's. His goal celebration was, to put it politely, exuberant. A full on sprint from the corner flag to the halfway line while cupping his left ear to onlookers, St Mary's fans in rapture, Renewal supporters bemused and affronted. It was a great goal but an inadvisable celebration, he'd take a few rough tackles after that spectacle.

There were about ten minutes to go when a Renewal corner was powered towards goal from the head of their big number nine, Geff in goal making a tremendous save to push it around the corner. The resultant corner was cleared and as Jack raced towards goal, the Renewal keeper raced out of his box to challenge him, the two crashing into each other but critically, the keeper was deemed to have handled the ball outside his box and somewhat harshly, was ordered off, serenaded by a sad lament from the buglers behind the opposite goal which raised a smile from all but the Renewal players. They were down to ten men and an outfielder was saddled with the keeper's shirt, bizarrely they selected the smallest guy on the pitch to go between the sticks. He acquitted himself pretty well until left stranded when a desperate charge from Renewal broke down with all of their players upfield in search of a last gasp equaliser, and substitute Tink broke away to loft the fourth goal into the net. 4-2, game over, St Mary's FC the Cup Winners 2007.

Supporters and players congregated in and around the stand by the halfway line as presentations were made by Tony Skelton shortly after the final whistle. First up was the referee, roundly booed as is the custom, second John Myatt who'd been nominated Man Of The Match (I remind you again that I taught him all there is to know about defending during my time at St Marys', clearly he had the good sense to ignore every word) and then it was the turn of a delighted Nick Sprason to be presented with the cup which he held proudly aloft. Who'd have thought it, St Marys FC, for so many years the wooden spoon contestants, now with the Cup trophy sat in the cabinet. I was chuffed for them, they deserved their night of glory. I politely turned down the after-show celebrations to be staged at Snobs nightclub in Birmingham. Carnage on the football pitch I'm accustomed to, carnage in Birmingham boozers after a cup final success was not something I was keen to witness.

CHAPTER TWENTY SIX

"... even though it's complicated, we got time to start again..."

There was a rumour going around at the Cup Final in the week, one that put a whole new complexion on today's final league game of the season where we found ourselves playing away at Dynamo Kingswinford. We thought our promotion hopes were dead and buried, and looking at the league table we had every reason to believe this — one game left, four points behind third spot and only three teams going up, but a glint of light could now be seen. Two new clubs had applied to join the league next season and by league convention, new clubs automatically went into the second division. As a result, it was proposed that an extra club may be promoted from the second division, that club being the one lying in fourth position. The league table reading as follows, we still had a chance —

	Played	Points	Goal Diff
Rowley College	16	44	+43
City Church	17	39	+36
Dynamo Kingswinford	16	34	+28
Us	17	30	+16
Halesowen Zion	17	29	+12

Fifth placed Halesowen Zion also had a chance. If they won their final match (against unbeaten champions Rowley) and we didn't, they'd leapfrog over us and claim the last promotion place. If it existed, which it might not. So it was a peculiar feeling entering the final day, perhaps having everything to play for, perhaps having nothing, no-one knew. It kind of suited us really, when a lot had ridden on a game this season we'd tensed up and arsed it up, it was preferable for us to enter the game believing it was meaningless, we'd have a better chance of success then.

And it came to pass, that after several weeks on the sidelines chomping at the bit, Ian Pearsall made his return to the WMCFL. His seven week ban had expired a couple of weeks prior but with him away working last week, he'd been unable to return until today. It had been touch and go as to whether he'd be selected. When he was red carded all those months ago at Amblecote, it seemed he'd never play for us again. The occasion was such an unpleasant one, he'd admit this himself, that there seemed no way back but to his enormous credit, he'd been full of remorse and attended every game since, so when Rob had a decision to make over whether to play Ian or not, there was a huge goodwill factor in his favour. There was only one match left, we hoped and prayed that Ian could keep a lid on his emotions to ensure we didn't receive the one yellow card that would tip us into the thirty disciplinary point abyss. He assured us there'd be no bother and we accepted this assurance.

Dynamo are a good side. Their attacking play is swift, just what a defender despises, and the interchanging between the strikers left Clem and me puzzled over who we should be marking. Pig was playing at right back for the first time ever, so his positional sense wasn't the greatest early on, and Daz had ditched his gleaming trainers for studded boots on a surface just as hard as last week, so he took time to find his feet. No surprise then that we fell behind to an early goal, nobody putting their hand up to track an onrushing midfielder who lashed a volley in from the edge of the box while the back four scratched their arses. One down and we'd been playing five minutes. We'd driven a long way to play this game, we weren't going to throw the towel in, so retaliated with sustained pressure of our own, Buzz running the midfield, spreading balls out to Pearsall on the right wing and Chas on the left, who provided mixed results. The final ball was somewhat lacking and their keeper seemed to gather most of them comfortably, he was a decent keeper too, it'd take a good goal to beat him. But that good goal soon came. Pearsall stood over a free kick about twenty five yards out and, Thierry Henry style, while the wall shuffled around with the keeper waiting for the ref to blow the whistle, he calmly passed it into the corner of the unguarded net. What a comeback for the great man, out for weeks but slotting in the equaliser on his return. He grinned at the keeper he'd just embarrassed, I thought he was going to give it the old wiggly fingers while his thumb touched the end of his nose, but he resisted the temptation and took the congratulations of his team-mates instead.

I was definitely going to be playing a whole game today, we only had eleven players. Preecey came along but wasn't playing due to a continued thigh problem, Joe and Nick were at a wedding, Andy Carter was going up to see Villa win at Man City and Chris Rogers had gone AWOL since the Brierley Hill match. So we were down to the bare bones, though my bones were far from bare thanks to the pounds of flesh I'd been piling on lately, eating unwanted easter eggs and not having trained for weeks. My lack of fitness was showing, I struggled to keep up as players ran with the ball, but I did enough today to make up for last week's shambles, just.

The game's decisive moment came shortly before half-time. Dynamo's left winger sidled into the box to commence an unsightly goalmouth scramble between three defenders and two attackers. The ball broke loose and as he ran forward to crack it into the net, he fell violently under the challenge of no-one in particular, not a defender within five yards of him, and a penalty was awarded. Bewildered players exchanged looks with the referee and with each other, silent in their shock, and a Dynamo defender crashed the spot-kick home after he'd been persuaded it wouldn't be a downright outrage to accept the penalty award. The ref went red and it wasn't due to sun burn, he'd dropped a clanger and no mistake. Yet that was that, there was no further scoring despite many chances from both sides, mostly ours. Mark Hadden scuffed a shot from ten yards into the goalie's hands, Tom Hathaway bladdered a volley attempt for a throw-in, Daz Smail screamed a long ranger over the bar and headed a corner straight at the keeper. Matt Brady had a couple of half chances but it became clear it wasn't going to be our day as the game went on. We rode our luck too, they hit the bar and shot wide a couple of times but the end of season feel was evident in the second half, especially when their keeper came out of goal to swap positions and play up front. I thought it was my birthday, he proved himself to be a keeper and not a striker in no uncertain terms during his cameo performance, ambling about without breaking into a jog once.

With five minutes remaining and the ball in Rob's hands in goal, the most contentious moment of the game had the two teams at loggerheads. Ian Pearsall was stood on the right wing by the halfway line, unmarked and in acres of space, yelling for Rob to deliver the ball to him. Rob couldn't hear him and bounced the ball a couple of times, oblivious to the increasingly loud demands from Pearsall to have the ball bowled out to his feet. Pearsall's frustration got the better of him and when Rob eventually clattered the ball forward, he let out an expletive audible in Tipton five miles away. Dynamo were in uproar, demanding the ref deal with the bad language according to the letter of the law, that's to say send him off. The ref allowed play to go on but still our opponents harangued the ref, urging him to discipline Pearsall until the ref stopped play and advanced towards Ian. I was furious. Not so much with Ian, he'd been exemplary today in his attitude and behaviour, and avoided confrontation a couple of times where the old Pearsall would have risen to the bait. No, I was angry with Dynamo for encouraging the ref to discipline Ian, we'd deeply appreciated his commitment since the ban, and warmly welcomed his return, but now it looked like the season would end disastrously for him and us. I grabbed one of their main antagonists and put him straight over what I thought of their protestations, he offered a mealy mouthed excuse for their behaviour and I was having none of it. "Ridiculous that a player should be sent off for language" he pined while with his next breath pleading with the ref to do something about it. We have much debate within the league about the whys and wherefores about red carding players for bad language, some say it's petty and unlikely to attract new teams and players, others suggest it shows an integrity in the league that few others can boast. Either way, when a player does let the odd f***ing w***er or sh**headed pr*** go, it's for the referee to deal with and not a protest lobby lead by half of the other team's players. In my opinion, foul and abusive language should be punished in the Christian league and that's not me getting up on my high horse, I just feel that it's a justifiable rule considering the context of the league and its foundations. Not everyone agrees, I don't expect them to, but when a player does swear I don't think it's acceptable for a team to pressure the ref to order him off.

Pearsall got away with it. The referee approached him after the finger pointing subsided and in all honesty I don't think he heard what Ian had said or Ian would have been a goner. The game got a bit feisty after that but didn't boil over, neither did it produce another goal. We'd played our last game of the season and we'd lost it, but put in a good performance, a positive note to pick up on at the beginning of the next campaign. My knee had been gashed for the last time this season, Clem had shouted his last words of encouragement, Buzz performed his last block tackle, Daz heaved his last through ball forward, Pig scurried up the wing one last time, Brady ripped off his shirt to show his rippling muscles, Mark Hadden kicked the turf in frustration, Matt Challoner megged his last meg, Tom Hathaway wailed his last long range shot over the bar and Rob ignored Pearsall's demands for the ball one final time. The season was finished, the tangerine dream would have to wait four more months before gracing the pitches of the West Midlands Christian Football League again. We'd be back, stronger, fitter and more determined.

We hoped the league might allow our fourth position in the table to represent the final promotion place, (Halesowen in fifth place had been gubbed 9-2 by Rowley so hadn't leapfrogged us), but accepted this to be unlikely. No worries, we'd walk the second division next season, with our without my sorry arse.

Final League Table

Rowley College	48
City Church	42
Dynamo Kingswinford	38
Us	30
Halesowen Zion	29
Zion Athletic	23
St Boniface	17
Brierley Hill AOG	12
Selly Oak Methodist	11
Walsall Olympic	5

CHAPTER TWENTY SEVEN

EPILOGUE

You know those housey programmes where they take a couple out to Spain for a week's house hunting, people who are yearning to leave the UK and start again? Nine times out of ten, after you've afforded them your emotional engagement for a good hour and watched them cry over the trauma of having to leave their family behind, the closing credits tell you the couple had a change of heart and decided to remain in their Doncaster bungalow. You feel cheated don't you? A waste of a programme, a pointless investment of your time and an altogether unsatisfactory outcome. Well, in the spirit of Channel 4's *A Place In The Sun,* I find myself confessing to a similarly anti-climactic ending. I started the book planning to account for St Thomas' march to promotion and must end it confirming that our fourth position was not sufficient for us to sneak our way into the First Division. Sorry and all that. Personally, I blame our strikers for not scoring enough goals, our keeper for conceding too many, and the midfield for the dearth of defence splitting passes which, had the manager possessed the good sense to play me up front, I'd have crashed into the net on a regular basis.

Any ineptitude displayed by my good self during the course of the season was purely in order that I might have sufficient material to write about. In truth, I am a world beater of epic proportions, have had trials at Old Trafford but turned them down and taught Paul McGrath all he knew. No-one likes a show off so I've kept all of this under my hat. Until now.

CHAPTER TWENTY EIGHT

POSTSCRIPT

Chapter headings are all lyrics from Teenage Fanclub tracks...

"*...come on over, the future's here...*" (Fallen Leaves)

"*...try to change what I've become...*" (Happiness)

"*...we're goin' over the country and into the Highlands to look for a home...*" (Planets)

"*...asked you for nothing, that's what I got...*" (The Cabbage)

"*...you were on the straight and narrow, you were going round the bend...*" (Straight And Narrow)

"*...don't look back on an empty feeling...*" (Don't Look Back)

"*... and it's no good, it's no good, it's no good...*" (Cul De Sac)

"*...Jesus Christ is knocking at my door...*" (Guiding Star)

"*...I love this life and all it's shown...*" (Nowhere)

"*...no matter what you do, it all returns to you...*" (Gene Clark)

"*... everything I want's within my grasp, it's time to nail my colours to the mast...*" (Flowing)

"*...there is more to learn than I aim for...*" (Time Stops)

"*...all my life I've felt so uptight, now it's all alright...*" (My Uptight Life)

"*...I was a stone I didn't show emotion...*" (It's All In My Mind)

"*...and I'm finding it so hard to stay in tune...*" (Dumb Dumb Dumb)

"*...a chance to start again and wipe the slate...*" (Flowing)

"*...we're together, on our way...*" (Norman 3)

"*...take the straight line, feel the sunshine...*" (Feel)

"*...and it's no wonder you can't stand on your own two feet...*" (Golden Glades)

"*...I don't need an attitude, rebellion is a platitude...*" (Verisimilitude)

"*...it's me for you & you for me...*" (I'll Make It Clear)

"*...trying to be someone I know I'm not...*" (Mellow Doubt)

"*...life feels so worthwhile when I go where you send me...*" (Near You)

"*...you're the future and I'm with you...*" (Norman 3)

"*...even though it's complicated, we got time to start again...*" (Start Again)

www.saltmine.org

Saltmine Trust is a charitable company limited by guarantee that was established in 1980. It quickly grew and today is a leading Christian organisation employing over 30 people at its Dudley, UK, Head Office.

Saltmine is at the forefront of Christian service, totally committed to evangelism, mission and the integrity of the family. Its Theatre Company, Red Balloon Theatre Company and Exalt Ministries, supported by Technical Services Department, regularly present the gospel in churches, schools, colleges, prisons, youth clubs and universities. They also feature at the many summer holiday initiatives of Saltmine.

Internationally, Saltmine has been committed to Eastern Europe since the 1970's. The principle ministry is in Bulgaria where Saltmine is involved in teaching programmes, support for building projects in churches and children's homes and organising humanitarian aid.

www.thehothouse.org.uk

What is the Hothouse?

It's a bright, welcoming place for children and families to enjoy.

Why is the Hothouse here?

It's here to help provide Community facilities in the heart of the Redhouse area of Aldridge, Walsall and to share the Good News of Christianity which we believe everyone deserves an opportunity to hear, experience, and respond to.